The Letter

ANGELA MORGAN CUTLER

TWO RAVENS
PRESS

Published by Two Ravens Press Ltd.
Taigh nam Fitheach
26 Breanish
Uig, Isle of Lewis
HS2 9HB

www.tworavenspress.com

The right of Angela Morgan Cutler to be identified as author
of this work has been asserted by her in accordance with the
Copyright, Designs and Patent Act, 1988.
© Angela Morgan Cutler, 2011.

ISBN: 978-1-906120-52-8

British Library Cataloguing in Publication Data: a CIP record
for this book can be obtained from the British Library.

Designed and typeset in Sabon by Two Ravens Press.
Cover design by Two Ravens Press.

Front cover image: *Envelope* by Gaillard, Didier (b.1953).
Private Collection/ C Special Photographers Archive/ The
Bridgeman Art Library. Nationality / copyright status: French
/ out of copyright.

Printed in Poland on Forest Stewardship
Council-accredited paper.

The publisher gratefully acknowledges subsidy from the
Scottish Arts Council towards the publication of this volume.

About the Author

Angela lives with her two teenage sons and husband Ian. She worked for ten years as a psychiatric nurse, trained as a fine artist and went on to complete a Ph.D. in Critical & Creative Writing. She has been running creative writing groups since 2000. *Auschwitz*, her first book, was published by Two Ravens Press in 2008.

For more information about the author, see
www.tworavenspress.com

Acknowledgements

My thanks to Claire Stewart, Roz Hall and Sarah Briggs for their encouragement and reading of early pages. To Mary Spaeth, Sarah Wild and Raymond Federman, who, despite the distance, are close by each day.

Special thanks to the people who generously shared their stories and allowed me to place those stories throughout this book, especially to the postmen, the police officer, dear Mary G – no better woman; thanks to Gerallt Nash, St Fagans Museum, for kindly sharing archive material, and to Sharon and David for their ongoing belief in the genreless book.

Certain longer passages in this book are taken from the titles listed below and are published here with the kind permission of the following publishers: *Death in the Afternoon*, Ernest Hemingway, Arrow Books (Random House), 2004; *Love Itself in the Letterbox*, Hélène Cixous, Polity Press (rights: Editions Galilée), 2008; *Species of Spaces*, George Perec, Penguin Classics, 1997; *The Gift of Fear*, Gavin De Becker, Little Brown & Company, 2000.

On finishing this book, I came across two other victims of threat letters whom I want to acknowledge. Bart Simpson, who received a death threat written in blood, and Knut the polar bear cub (care of the Berlin Zoo) who received an anonymous threat that read, "Knut is dead! Thursday midday." Thursday came and went. Knut – and Bart – are both safe and well. Knut became so famous as a result of the threat that his image was issued on a German postage stamp.

This book is for Ian
Luke, Seth & Max

For my mother
And for my father who loves to tell stories
and loves to laugh

Only that which is absent can be imagined.
Proust

Dead / pulverised / molested
animals seem to be
recurrent trope.

Food, animals,
  consumption

I was in the bedroom when he phoned.

When En read your letter to me for the first time. I was in the bedroom standing on my left leg, my right knee pressed into the bed wondering how many dead geese it had taken to fill our four pillows, a whole new king-size duvet, the soft places of a bird, a house, a body.

No, a lie, rather a mismemory of events: I had gone upstairs, who knows why. I was ringing En, ringing him at The Quad where he worked. Yes, I'm sure that's how it was. And after a while I was speaking and getting the impression that he wasn't really listening – you know that feeling, that sense of the other being preoccupied, elsewhere, saying yes and no, but you can tell they're not really concentrating. I gave it time, rattled on because I had, I felt, something important to tell him. – Forget it! I said, feeling suddenly foolish. I can be as petulant as the rest. Standing on my left leg, my right knee pushed into the mattress of our bed, supporting myself like some kind of flamingo, when he did something I'd never known – *that got my attention* – not in our twenty-three years of phoning each other from home, from work: he started to cry…

I am sure it was then that I positioned myself deep inside the goose down in order to take whatever was coming, whatever he was going to say next, as I knew it would be something out of the ordinary that day, midday, almost time for a sandwich, almost the time of day when En would call and say – I'm walking to the canteen, I'm off to get a bite to eat, a roll, some fish with mash, nothing much. He'd tell me things like this; and me, sometimes I'd ring him up in the middle of *very important meetings*, I'd ring him up and I'd say things like, what shall we have for tea, or can you pick up a cauli on the way home – yes, lamb chops from the butcher… Do you see, and I've got quite a reputation for ringing him up at The Quad

3

and others laughing and saying – There she goes again, we're in the middle of some life-or-death corporate decision and there she goes talking chops, bread, onions... But we like to check in with each other at least once a day, at least once a day so we can tell each other what we'll eat or what we're about to eat, how we miss each other, how we'll ring again around four, just checking in – yes, this is how we are.

It isn't normally like that when I ring; I mean, in spite of whatever meeting or agenda or corporate business is underway, it isn't normal for him not to listen, for him to speak to me but sound so far away, for us not to get down to the food part, for him to cry on the phone – *softly*, I should tell you – and not for himself, but more with the burden of telling what he did not want me to hear, small moments held on the tongue, in the choice of how to, if to, when to, the hovering and misconstrued hesitation, the silence marked by the words of your letter pressed into all that white space, a threat held in his hand, throat, heart, blood, gut, already that far inside, our mouths and ears pressed to one another through the distance of some miles, me at home, him at work, bed, desk, ear-to-ear in that moment just before what cannot be anticipated, your words passing through time – slowing time. Words passing from you to him, me to you, your letter in turn to be passed on and into our children's ears, our friends, neighbours, the whole paper chase and pass-the-parcel to come.

It is not easy to tell you this, you of all people. I almost crossed out the word *cry*, wiped away those few small tears on the page, XXed it out as you had XXed out part of the letter. I should tell you that En's crying was almost inaudible, never really got going, was not announced or named or spoken of – but over the years you come to know the sounds the other makes when you have spent a lifetime listening to his sleeping, waking, breathing, laughing, moaning, loving, teasing, shouting,

4

silent sounds: sounds that get inside your body, your ear still to the phone, you get to know the rhythm he makes, the way his voice lilts, the way he has of saying, – Wait ... I have something to tell you ... Something I don't want to tell you ...

But as you wrote in your letter ...

I'll get to the point ...

Visualise this:

En whispering your letter to me, not wanting anyone to overhear your words repeated, hushed words. Remember he was at work, at The Quad, his voice over the phone almost a torch under the goose-down duvet, my ear wanting to close on the word hurt, your words received where and when you least expect it into my right ear. I had no thought of guns. I went straight for the weapon I feared most, to the parts of the body that I loved most: head, chest, belly; a long sleek blade, bone-handled; I saw him stabbed, already dead. Like one of those games of *Cluedo* – only this time off the board – when, at age eleven, I'd always chosen to be Miss Scarlet. Miss Scarlet with the rope in the kitchen. Back then, as now, I'd never have picked the knife. The tiny rope that frayed over time. Kitchen, billiard room, ballroom, it all came rushing back ... The Reverend Green, Colonel Mustard, non-playing murder victim ... The TV programme I had watched only that week: *How To Write a Murder Mystery – Top Tips ... Choose a credible murder; select your weapon.*

– What did you visualise ... someone later asked me ... when En rang with news of the letter. What did you see?

My eyes were watching the tree move beyond the window, up high, the nest swaying, so vulnerable, yet so well made. The crows flew away together, they'd been patient until my eyes caught the sun in the leaves, until somewhere beyond the word hurt a bird broke in two. I couldn't be more candid. It couldn't have been more intimate, the room, the bed, duvet, feathers, and phone. He talked, I listened, details given: the threat had gone unnoticed for some days. We'd come to know that thirteen people had handled the letter at The Quad where En worked, thirteen people, thirteen years he'd worked there, one person's hands for every year of work. The thirteen included the workers at The Quad's own post room, during that delay when we didn't know what you'd written. The police had only just taken away the letter, the brown envelope, handwritten, the letter duplicated ad infinitum on a photocopier, but not the envelope. Instead the envelope was placed in a plastic bag – you know the sort – the ones with the re-sealable edge, the ones people use for sandwiches. People gathered around while someone held it at the corner of the plastic and peered in, the way you might examine a new goldfish, but with less of a smile. The envelope, I assume, was brown. I don't know why I assume; maybe because it was sent to work, about work, most likely via someone at work. I like the word *manila*. I prefer white envelopes; white envelopes make it seem as if you've tried a bit harder, elevated the letter to something more personal, yet the words have less of a ring than *manila*, the envelope, the letter written by an anonymous other, you on that old manual typewriter. They made copies of the letter, the police, The Quad, En, before the original was sent off to the lab. The language you hear in films: lab, fingerprints, crime scene; the almost clichéd use of a manual typewriter ... The signature of course omitted ...

There were spelling mistakes in the letter, which all the experts said looked suspicious, inconsistent with the idea that a destitute person – so-called – had written it. Written it in order to stop any changes being made to the team. The team you said had saved my life. The team that The Quad had wanted to 'restructure' ... I don't know if you can stop this closure,

6

the letter said. Not closure, *re-structure,* The Quad said. The
mud crabs of The Quad, my son calls them, the workers carrying
out and caught up in the usual politics and slight nuances of
language, semantics, the usual dirty underwear common to all
institutions, learning, caring, producing, ducking and diving,
wheeling and dealing, and En, you could say, caught in the
middle, doing his job, the usual annual budget deficits, cost-
cutting, corporate re-orderings, spring-cleaning, but if you
don't change this, as I am told you can, be very sure
you will be hurt. Not very soon but in the right time.
This will give me and my collleages [more misspellings]
even more pleasure when you meet up with us. We
really could spoil your comfartable life ...

The fart did not go unnoticed; more in keeping, they said
– the experts – with someone trying to create the idea that an
uneducated person sent this; the whole thing inconsistent, they
said: someone from work, no doubt, someone educated trying
to sound as if they are uneducated.

I thought of my own misspelling, I thought [thougt] of
myself in school, maybe nine, ten years old, the teacher standing me on a chair for my page of errors, failed weekly tests.
Each week toppling on the chair, the views from there, the tops
of others' heads, the good spellers with their polished Clarke's
shoes safely on the ground. I wondered what people were now
saying, with their so-called insights, about the letter's spelling;
what we want to believe of education and deceit, of lies and
manipulations, the whys and wherefores, to know when and
if an educated person can spell and an uneducated cannot ...
surely more to it than that.

I wondered about that word hurt that lingered – hurt
repeated – harm repeated, I would like to be able to give
you my name, but that would put me in harms way ...
but for sure you will be hurt, when you least expect it,

when you think you are out of the woods but aren't.

Almost the child's ring to it – the woods – the teddy bears' picnic, the trees I grew up beside, loved in, cried in, hid inside, made dens in, [make haste], frightened myself half to death in, the menace of the wood, a whole wood drawn into a letter or a letter drawing us inside a wood: Ms White's heart collected in a box; Ms Gretel's edible house, the oven, the stew pot. *If you go down to the woods today*; Beckett's: *a kiss makes an indescribable sound.*

The call, the letter, you might say, forced me to stop writing a book. A book I had been working on about my son, all fiction, a book about voyeurism, the voyeurism I had imagined now turned on its heels, now turned on to us. Me at the window – *Windows*, by coincidence the title of the book – just me at the window already wondering if we were being watched. In the instant of the letter's appearance everyone came under suspicion, even people like the new neighbours we didn't know too well, people hanging around by the riverbank where we live. The window cleaner is new, the postman is no longer anticipated in the same way. Yes, after En called me – or was it me who called him? – I sat on the bed for some time after he read the letter to me and I didn't know what to say or do, whom to tell, how to tell. When I found a way to move my legs and arms and do the things I so normally take for granted, I made some tea. Tea, that's what happens at a time like this; all day in fact our red kettle is never left to cool for long, it purrs on the small Aga, it waits for a break in words so I can replenish myself without delay. This day, no longer a normal day, [all I'd forgotten in a moment], except the word hurt poured out with the steam of the kettle, the steam people sometimes use to open letters they are not supposed to read, steamed-up windows lacing me in from the threats that were now upon us. Tea in hand, the word hurt written into condensation, the word hurt looked up.

v., **hurt, hurt·ing, hurts.**

v.tr.

1. To cause physical damage or pain to; injure.

2. To cause mental or emotional suffering to; distress.

3. To cause physical damage to; harm: The frost hurt the orange crop.

4. To be detrimental to; hinder or impair: The scandal hurt the candidate's chances for victory.

n.

1. Something that hurts; a pain, injury, or wound.

2. Mental suffering; anguish: getting over the hurt of reading the letter.

3. A wrong, harm: What hurt have you done to them?

Yes, I made tea, saying to myself that if I had not been alone that day, if someone had been with me when I received the news, the hurt, the threat, then they would have put on the kettle. A lump of chocolate for the shock, I said to myself … that's what people do. Suck on something sweet, sometimes people even wash your clothes, cook for you, a surge of activity, festivity hidden away inside a crisis. There's the buzz of action, doing, sorting, fixing, fight or flight, the kettle begins some sense of commemoration, however present the loss, the loss of a life, of a routine, a freedom you took for granted, if not some marked sense of the disorientation that comes from an intimacy, out of a moment, event, words sent your way.

When someone died once – well, the promise of a child I'd conceived and lost, remember that – a group of friends came by, brought me flowers, brewed up all day, pegged out my washing, made a lamb casserole, the red marbled meat in L's hands. Later she ironed my towels. I watched her and heard myself say, I never iron towels. They whispered a lot out of a kind of reverence, as if the volume of speech had suddenly

9

become too brittle and coarse to be spoken in normal tones. I had nowhere to go while they filled the house, took over the kitchen, made me a cake. I'll go back to this later: tea, cake, the impulse we have to do something basic when something happens, to turn all you took for granted into a casserole with carrots, the impulse to bake, to brew, to steam, wash, press, sweep, make love – as I write this a woman who conceived her son the night of 9/11 is saying on the news that the birth rate went up around that time, yes, following any tragedy we have the urge to reproduce, she says, to replicate ourselves in another. And at that time, when the house was full of friends – not now; pre-letter, way back – I went to the local shop to get away from the gathering in my kitchen, to get a moment's peace. I knew they meant well. I told the woman on the vitamin counter everything about the house filled with people, the smell of baking, flour everywhere, the hundreds-and-thousands, the empty unused cot. She sat me on a stool and she too made me tea. She added the sugar I never take, and it formed into syrup at the bottom. In the end it was time to go home and drink more tea, to see my friend cleaning my potato peeler. That's how it goes: one minute people are strangers, then over time you find yourselves spending the odd evening together, which becomes a routine, an occasional meal, conversations, cheese on toast, a walk and life's stories and things in common like writing and laughing at the same TV programmes, the misfortunes, the next, your own; no one's laughing, and there they are, these people you know but have never seen like this before, there they are washing up your wooden spoons, rifling in your cupboards, wearing your apron, taking your underwear off the line, folding it into a basket.

Yes, to go back…

I went to the search engine, post-En's call, about the letter that was causing me to move around rooms, pacing from here to there no longer knowing where my destination was. I closed down the book I was writing about my son, indirectly – you know, the one about looking and being looked at, about absence; all this inspired by my son's announcement that he would soon be leaving home. It's the way, the normal thing, people said. I'd promised him I'd teach him how to cook, wash clothes, clean, basic things. We had a year or two before he might be on his way. It made me want to write as if he were already on his way to who knows where. It would be a book loosely based around his going, a book that would include the recipes I'd teach him, maybe – who's to know. I had written no more than forty pages. Forty pages that I closed down when I made myself tea, post-letter, the day of the letter. I closed down my work and instead went into the search engine and put in the word Hurt. Hurt ending in bruise, in fingerprints pressed into flesh, in the contradiction of the beautiful colour blue, *azul*; azure, plum blue.

I wondered a lot about the delay, the delay between you writing the letter and En receiving it. That gap ... like when you go under the knife, in hospital let's say, and there you are being filled with anaesthetic and it is pleasant enough, the journey it makes up your arm and through you ... and there you are wearing one of those ridiculous hats trying not to care about how you look, telling yourself to just keep counting, counting, and there you are: count down, as if you are back in school and no more than a child again, first lessons, 9, 8, 7, as if you are about to launch into space, traverse the moon... And where are we then, *where do you go to my lovely*... That's what I wondered about, that gap, as I copied down the translations, the meanings of hurt, past and present, formal, nouns, verbs (orig. 'to strike' 'a blow'). I wondered about that time when you

11

knew about us and we knew nothing of you or your letter. For you, a delicious space – *Or am I being unfair, presuming too much* ... The time when we knew nothing, you knew everything of our time to come.

Forgive the repetition but when I first heard of the letter I was in the bedroom...

I'll try to slow down. I have a tendency to rush ahead. The letter did that to me: quickened everything, you might say. You might say that when En read me your words over the phone I was wearing my funeral hat, matching shoes, a ribboned simple black dress. In retrospect, it is easy to laugh at all this – are you laughing too? Some might say that I have a tendency to exaggerate. I write for a living – not in the financial sense, more in a living, must-do sense, for now – to make sense of you, to make sense for you. To fill in the gaps of what must have been left to your imagination, post-letter. You imagining us, we imagining you, and all that we cannot know of each other, all our befores-and-afters, all you couldn't have known: that I write for a living. Maybe you do too, maybe that's the clue, maybe you too have the pen-man about you, or in this case, that old typewriter you'd kept in an attic maybe, for decoration perhaps, the way people keep old tills and stuffed parakeets, thimbles, bells... My mother kept bells, bells and shire horses and pottery, hats, tins of buttons, always buttons, a whole selection box. I have, like so many, always kept letters of course, love and otherwise, ribboned like the dress, tied and knotted and classified and lofted, boxed, Sellotaped and drawered. Yes, some keep old phones and even phone boxes, but you'd need the space for a thing that size; keeping your old typewriter makes more sense, I can see that. I can see in that way we are alike. There's something romantic about those old typewriters that you don't find in any kind of computer, however swish or high-tech; no, there's something in the colour green that is ours, the one we kept, just like you. The keys, the paper bail, platen, wind around ribbons, the word ribbon; pleasure of the word, the sound of Krapp's S P O O L S, the pleasure of the red and black ribbon selector, QWERTY layout, carriage return, margin stops, paper arm. Line space. Next line...

You never know when you will need those old things that we all too easily discard. We hoard and worry, worry and hoard. In that way maybe we are alike. I am guessing – it's all guesswork here. That's what happens when you make yourself a fiction. I do it all the time, it's a way of life for me, that's what I said, a life where you decide to write. One day, one evening maybe... When you wrote En a letter, a letter to *us*, plural – he does not live alone, you knew that much. Which made the threat worse, the not knowing who you were, the guessing, the imagination, the fictions, the violence that not-knowing forms. Fear, you might say, makes a killer out of me. Makes me act out in images all that you threatened. My imagination makes me an unexpected accomplice. The letter setting off a whole reserve of scenarios in me, in us, so that we kill En, injure him at least every ten minutes to begin with, each hour, at least once a day, especially at night – yes, nights are worse, the dark, the leaps, the creeks of the stairs, the windows, back to that, the stray alley-cat's wail, people somewhere screaming, whistling, the stars overhead lighting up nothing except our imagination, joining up the dots all wrong with fear and acting out all the potential hurts a threat can carry; the knowing that you knew us, En at least, that you knew where we lived, had done your homework, your groundwork, mapping our geography; we, plunged into the world of what if, could be, so many grotesque possibilities in all directions.

Yes, like you, I would have used that old typewriter. As

much as it would vex me along the way to go back to that machine, that old iron ho. If I'd used our old typewriter to write you a letter – the machine that I have to tell you he wrote his way through a divorce on – En that is, way back, over twenty years back, the hours, the careful arrangement of words selected – who hasn't done this, who hasn't written confessions, job applications, declarations of love; who hasn't typed and retyped those carefully worded pleas to orders, the court appeals, the anguish, the correction fluid, the time spent hunched over the beast, to write his way through and on, trying to get something across – if, like you, I'd found myself using that same old typewriter we had put away in the loft; if, like you, I'd found myself going back to that old machine in the evenings, to type you a letter, a reply of sorts, the way I now find myself trying to convey something to you, something heard, whispered, known between us, some little response; if I had been you, in your shoes and socks, or sandals, or slippers, or like me, bare-footed in the evenings… Yes, it occurred to me that if I had written this letter on such an old machine, then surely I would have taken more care to get the letter right. Maybe – I'm guessing, who can know or judge – but maybe I might have found myself rewriting it again and again if I'd made mistakes [the paper that would have been required], the patience to avoid the XXXXs you added, the XXXs crossing words through, covering over words you wanted to obliterate or draw attention to – either way, we tried hard to decipher each kiss – all of it adding to the fiction. Either way, the kisses of course only emphasised the error of a human hand, the slip of thought, the time passed since you were at one with the machine; or perhaps, as some implied, only added to the illusion of error … everything, I suspect, was thought through, like the kisses that normally go at the end, or X marks the spot. Yes, I suspect that if it were me I would have written the letter over

14

and over until I got it right, my tongue to the corner of my mouth, cold tea to my side in a mug, no cigarettes, not now ...

Maybe you smoke, maybe it was late when you wrote so you poured yourself a drink – whisky perhaps, or brandy – but not for me – for me it's tea at that hour, camomile, ginger with sorrel, Dr Stuart's Night Time Tranquillity, loose-leaf, a pot, a strainer, the mess beside me, notes everywhere, that's how I am, notes, tea going everywhere, going over and over things, more corrections, abandoned attempts screwed up on the floor ... it's tiring, I tell you; it's time-consuming and gut-wrenching; it's lab-bore-ious.

I imagine it was evening when you wrote. Lamplight, the moon watching through the window, everyone else asleep, clear view, steady speed; nearby, next door the comfort of those lost to dreams. En too, some way off, away from you, beside me. He sleeps well at night, better than me, before the letter, since the letter, he slept on, imagine! Unlike me, who after you wrote took on the job of listening out, for better, for worse, poorer for the worry, the wanting to keep him safe, all that, but to get back to the letter, to that old typewriter ...

Back and forth with the bell. The bell and the keys hurting your fingers and the resistance of the spring, and the little bottles of correction fluid you didn't use, maybe for obvious reasons ... yes, just imagine if you had, imagine all of us over your letter scratching away at what lies beneath ... what a sight, what scraping, what knife edges, what impatience and overcrowding to see what was hidden beneath a stroke of white. Carbon paper – yes, remember that – it just came back to me with a rush staining my fingers blue, purple-blue carbon paper.

I wondered did you keep your own copy – of the letter, that is; the finished article. In spite of the obvious risk I am sure I'd have kept a copy, somewhere hidden, somewhere carefully folded and halved and quartered, a tiny folded page slid inside a book, under a stone, under the mattress, inside a pocket, inside the hole of a china cat.

Maybe you were drunk. I've written into this tale a bottle of whisky, hip flask, shot glasses, whatever you'd prefer. The amber caught in the light pulled low over the old typewriter. Maybe one became two, three became five, five small tots, no ice. Maybe it's safer to think of you that way for the time being, at the time of writing, with the responsibility, and the impulse, or meditation, the planning, the buildup, the malice, the energy or the gravity it takes – who wouldn't need or deserve a drink. I've given you a get-out clause; alcohol can do that, make you act on whatever impulses have been swilling in the mind, the pacing and the time it took and the whisky tumblers lining up beside the typewriter. Maybe the night of the letter you didn't bother with the best glasses; maybe you used the coffee cups, the tea mugs, or straight from the bottle, swigging the drink and the anger and what fear, what longing, what loneliness, misdoing that drove you to wait until everyone was asleep to take the ladder from the shed, get the machine down from the loft, compose all that had brewed in you for weeks, months, who could ever know. All you had scribbled onto scraps, bus tickets, till receipts. I'm this way myself, all these things pop into my head, during the day, all night, the sentences that come to you both formed and virginal, if language can ever be that innocent; soon forgotten if you don't get it down, somewhere, anywhere, whatever you can find, even in the dark sometimes, even on the toilet roll…

Someone told me that once, the story of the toilet paper she'd written on … how she'd come to that … I'll tell you what happened …

A woman I met very briefly, for two hours, to be exact – people tell me the most intimate of things in the most unlikely of places, over the frozen-fish counter, or at the park, while sitting on a bench writing – yes, we met on a bench; she was feeding some stray cats with bits of old Hovis bread. She specified the make. It didn't take her long to get past her choice of whole-meal, her list of symptoms, the weather, the usual patter and onto her husband that was. And when she saw me with my small notebook, she told me the story of how her husband had died, openly enough, she told me everything without faltering, without looking at me. We were both facing a rather elaborate pampas grass when she explained how her husband, several years back, had fallen from a ladder – a stepladder, to be precise. He wasn't drunk, it was breakfast time; she had only just cleaned away the table they'd shared by the window, cleaned up the remains of the boiled eggs they'd eaten, three-minute eggs, the little crumbs the soldiers made, the yellow all over the empty shell, the little hat of shell he'd forgotten to scoop out. His last words were – Put the kettle on. He was unblocking ivy from the guttering, nothing glamorous. Often our last moments are laughable, absurd; if only we knew in advance. Think of Elvis on the loo … *maybe don't*. It was laughable, she said, except as the kettle reached its climax, as she turned off the din, brewed up, settling back to the silence, she went to call him, she went to call his name and instead she heard the crack. The crack of the egg, the crack as he fell and she knew that he'd broken his neck though she hadn't realised it was so easy to break a neck from a small fall, at such an ordinary hour of the day, with the tea stewing, never touched.

– And for months after, she said, I was so immersed in my grief, waking at all hours, and in desperation I'd write to him: messages, love poems, letters telling him how much I missed him; when all the paper I could find had been filled with more and more words, I'd then sit on the bowl of the toilet and write to him. I even wrote on the toilet roll until the paper tore and then I'd begin again. The packs I got through, the kettle always on in the distance. I drank all the tea he never got to. All those soft scented notes saved up in a box. A box I'd have liked to show you if some weeks back I'd not decided it was best, best to move on – best burn the bloody lot.

Yes, the night of the letter maybe you burned the remains, notes, false starts, workings-out; you left no clue, nothing grand, no bonfires, just a saucer and matches, the grate and coals, last embers; only the letter survives. The typewriter put away again for who knows what would be its next call. The loft hatch secured, the last one for the road; one of those nights ... an exceptional night; there it was, the letter in your pocket.

Maybe you even walked the small half-mile to the post box that night to make sure no one saw, to make sure that it was done with, to make sure that you didn't change your mind, sunrise, sober mind, second thoughts; to see that it was finished and decided and over to us, the letter on its way, the letter making haste, god's speed; some air to shake off the whisky, to separate out the deed from sleep to come, a few hours left before sun-up. The walk to the box, the so-familiar route, red in the distance, moonlit, red deepening still under the dark sky, the moon you gazed at, wished upon, sighing at the stars, joining up the plough, the crab – my sign, you couldn't know that. You, looking at the empty roads, a stray dog roaming the night maybe raised his snout, too tired to cock a leg, only looked at you with half-turned eyes while you relieved yourself of the full bladder the whisky had produced. The sound of this slow ting-a-ling, tintinnabulation, beside the dog, time for that, while the letter, full of promise, tingled inside the dark trouser pocket, so much so that you felt its message was spreading itself through your whole body. The sensation of the letter against your leg as you readjusted your trousers. You could hear the noise it made as

18

you walked, a fine rhythm, no rush but on, on nearing the box, reciting each line quietly to yourself. The red began to greet you like an old friend, like an ally, your eyes bloodshot with tiredness, with the needed concentration the letter had taken from you; you could even taste red, the red inked letters on the envelope, red in your mouth repeating the words you'd formed, trying to recite each line, remember each line, each word, each XXX – the mistakes and the hurt and En's name

Dear Mr ...

Carefully placed in the left-hand corner.

Dear Mr ...

Repeated

Dear Mr ...

Left-hand side, the name. Yours XXXcluded. For my sake, you say. Dear Mr ... I would like to give you my name but I fear that would only put me in harm's way. Did you look up, as I did, the word hurt ... the word harm. Did you end on the word interest? Did you recheck the address, did you kiss it goodbye? Did you hear the blink of the crossing – hesitate as you faced the box, the no-going-back, hand, mouth, finger and thumb. Let it go ... Talk your way in. The letter dropping like a penny wish.

There is the time of my putting together this book a year after your letter had arrived.

Time present you could say, a time when En has found a new job, has long since escaped The Quad, freed himself of the threat. Time present when I begin gathering together all the small pieces I had written to you.

Then there is the time in Spain, weeks we spend in anonymity after months of feeling watched, vigilant, held hostage to your threat, a time when we find solace hidden in a small village where there is no fear of being found or approached or harmed. It is here I begin what I call the Day Pages, instigated by my usual patterns when away of daily writing in my notebooks. Early starts waking to an expanse of sky, sounds and smells, the unfamiliar that draws the pen to the page. That holiday Luke my stepson had joined us with our teenage boys, Hugo, and D. Every morning we'd sit and write, sometimes in our separate rooms, some mornings I'd wake and peer over the balcony of our rented house, and there would be Luke and Hugo already up and writing at the table in the small yard below. Their commitment to the word that holiday made me smile, surprised and touched me; their words that began to undo the words of your letter. Sun-up we'd write: the Waltons-come-Scheherazade. Each evening as the sun went down we'd sit and share those small tales, read each new version as the snacks came out. En close by, listening, D in the rocking chair he'd adopted, rocking in the doorway to the sound of our words.

At first it wasn't clear that I wanted to write to you at all, having no face for you, no name, no forwarding address, little story, for what is it that happened – post-letter, just the opening up of a response, just the fear that plagues the imagination, begins a letter that may never be read by the one I call You. We of

20

course had our suspicions of who you might be: those early weeks we talked of little else, but of course it shifts, it meanders, almost spoils what my imagination evokes. Imagination makes you mightier than the man, or men, whom we suspect sent the letter our way. I do not think of you as a woman – I will go on with that later. For now, I give you more than I could in person: in my fiction of you, you expand, rise, soar, you become something neither of us could have foreseen when we set out in each other's direction. You and I may never recognise ourselves here. Nameless being: Mary Shelley in her outhouse playing with her monster.

In spite of this, you could say, I have always held a fascination for epistolary. I am what you might call a responder. I address, as-sign, give myself the task and duty to allot myself to you. That is of course the way letters work, a kind of excessive talking to oneself that all letters contain – the anonymous threat is maybe an exception, has to find new forms, leaps in the dark, hallucinations, paranoia, in this case is it absurd to imagine there is anybody there? Yes, on the whole we receive a letter and that old knee-jerk is to reply. We read the letter we are already composing a yes, yes, yes, as clear as Molly Bloom. This yes, over time, becoming all the words that accumulate in your direction. Home, your letter arrives and pulls open all we take for granted in the security we feel when we close the door. Home, the safety we feel in bricks and concrete, in doors and double-glazed windows closed, or come to that, cast open to the air. The privacy we imagine for ourselves, our ability to leave home each day without concern, without asking who is behind us, following, watching, waiting to jump out.

Home, come and go, pen in hand.

Home as a place of rest, waiting, writing.

Home: place of person or family – where we live together – En, the two boys and me. At home, holiday home, here or

21

there, either place will do, a place to sleep and store and contain – sanitary enough, a place to prepare food.

Home: a place of refuge where worldly cares fade, or so it says in the big book of words…

I would begin this letter to you – this book to you – and give it such titles as *Mountain of the Dead Woman*. A mountain we travel to and from in the course of the weeks we spend in Spain. I could call this book to you *The Gold Room*. It could begin with the words I write from this room each morning when I wake with such happiness, such a rush of freedom, knowing we are safely tucked up and hidden away in a place you will never find us.

This is how it could begin – with the name of a small village that for weeks becomes a temporary shelter, a home of sorts, Adrada de Pirón. En, me and the three boys: Hugo, as my youngest son wants to be called here; D, remembering that when he was small we'd tag his name with Darling. How, those first days of school, he would argue without doubt that his surname was indeed Darling. When we'd insist it was now time to put aside foolish names, his hurt caused a retraction, caused us to double-barrel him, at least at home. Darling became D over the years, a trace of the original endearment.

Luke says he wants to be given – in this book at least – the name he had as a toddler, Snoopy the Bubble. I tell him it is cute but far too long. We end up with Bub for swiftness, but that doesn't last. For ease he returns to his birth name. We laugh together and discuss names, those early mornings in Spain, Luke and me sitting together downstairs while everyone is still half-asleep. Luke finds my notebook, asks if we can write together. He tells me that he wants to use the time we have here to write some lyrics for his guitar, to write some stories that he can turn into songs, to try to write each day. He asks me to read to him, read what I wrote this morning … asks who Adrada de Pirón is, – Is it your pen name? Not realising it is the name of the village where we are staying. He puts the question to me very seriously. – I like the sound of that name, he says. Maybe that's what you should remain in this story: Adrada de Pirón.

I tell him that by coincidence this morning I ended what I had written with a piece about names, wondering how to address the anonymous other of the letter, Dear Mr … A letter of sorts to the person who wrote the threat … to your father, I tell him. I explain that I do not want it to be an angry letter, maybe instead a love letter of sorts. – Is this possible, he asks. Could there be a right way to address you? To not sound off-key, ill-humoured, provoked… We make tea, Luke and me, we sit on the oversized sofas – one each – and I read the letter I have begun to you; small stories, meanderings, digressions abound while the other boys overhead are still asleep, while En joins us, potters in the small kitchen.

Day Pages – Spain

The Mountain of the Dead Woman is a range of mountains we pass each day. We are not looking for you here. Neither do we ask around. Here we are safe. I would not say that we don't talk about you any more. There are times we do, and will. Times when we do all we can to make light of it all. It is not a detective story. Before we left, in the early days of your letter, I'd watch En's eyes search crowds, sometimes fix on someone. Someone we'd pick out just for the hell of it – let ourselves toy with the idea that it was you, you alone, you with the men, you with another family, you, just feet away drinking a cognac with your morning coffee, or feeding your dog bread dipped in chocolate.

Here, our bedroom in the house we rented is gold. Our sons' rooms differing shades of blue. Each of their rooms has a small single bed and two shuttered windows. We kneel on the bed to look over the fields and from the bathroom watch the road wind into the distance between the hills. I lie in the bath and do the same. Watch the cars advance and depart as I soap my limbs. The odd donkey follows the road. Groups of old people out for their morning or evening strolls. It is from here that I begin to write to you, both my Day Pages and whatever words may come from this house that we borrow and, for now, make our own. As people do when they are away, we go on small excursions, mostly local, the parks, the museum, the woods, trains we take for the day, journeys that end in small towns, large cities, on the edges of the sea. We get used to the routine. It sets us on our way. The rest unfolds each day in a notebook I bought just for the task.

I woke early today to the distant and strangulated calls of a cockerel drawing up the hour, the coolness of the room, the silence of shuttered outlines, the window, wardrobe, the shadow of the chair, a ray of dust caught in sun. A whiff of cow shit mixes with the smell of cologne when still in my nightshirt I open up the window, breathe deeply, allow the sun to flood in. Carry forward the shadows of birds, birds flying the length of the wall. Look! The swallows are everywhere, celebrate return, their shadows hurl themselves around me.

This book – this book to you – could be called *The Left-Hand Pages,* as soft and as thin as the pages I begin to fill on the left side of my notebook, the left side where there is nothing to support my pen, unlike the delicious density of *The Right-Hand Pages*, thick empty whiteness – waiting – waiting –

It is then I remember a story.

Listen…

When I was around twelve, I was at a children's party. I don't know why, but I want to tell you this. I want you to know the digressions, the details that make up a life. I was at Adele's house. Michael was there. There was something very ordinary about Michael that I liked. Michael, you might say, had the mood of someone who had seen too much in his thirteen years – something in his straw hair, not a colour I normally desired – not dark enough – hair aside, something in his steadiness pleased me…

And as I begin to write this down, a voice interrupts – on the radio there's a man talking about numbers – yes, about his way with numbers, about his autism. En translating the parts I cannot understand, his Spanish is better. On the radio, the woman asks the man to figure out from her birth date what day of the week she was born. He does a speedy calculation and announces confidently: a Tuesday. – Same day as me, I say to En. – Tuesday's child is fair of face, he says. I twist up my eyes… – Not necessarily true, I tell him, as I recall it was Michael's not-so-fair face, other things perhaps, not the face, that I found appealing. Anyway, the autistic man goes on to

25

describe the days of the week as colours: Wednesday as azul, a beautiful word and colour. He describes how, when he was younger, he didn't understand people's need for friendship, until he reached the age of about twelve and decided that he too wanted to feel what friendship was like. Not understanding the need people have for borders, boundaries, distance, he said that he'd stand very close to people, so close that he could feel their body heat and that would arouse him. He was brave enough to use the word arouse. He'd feel pleasure just to be close enough to that change of temperature in them, in himself – too slight a thing for those who are no doubt rushing through life. He would move close enough to register the nuances, that stillness, so that they become measured, he said ... like mercury in glass.

In this way it was not Michael's face that drew me to him, rather a calmness he exuded which no doubt I could have measured *Like Mercury in Glass*, another possible title.

But for now...

At the children's party – back to that – people were taking it in turns to play that game, blind man's buff. You got to kiss in the darkness of Adele's hallway – no, more a narrow passage which brought people closer together whether they wanted it or not. What is a buff anyway, I'd wanted to ask Michael, whom I'd been teemed up with in the passageway. A kiss we somehow missed, the face that ended up in an ear, in hair, blind after all. We told no one, only took our turn back to the front room to allow the next couple through. We returned to the sofa and sat together while he asked me a question. A question so direct, so simple, that it derailed me – the question somehow finding its way through Michael's calmness, close enough now to feel the heart and the heat of the question rising. He found himself with a book – who can know any longer the name of such a book, how he found it beside him like that, a book abandoned to some coffee table, pulled from some old rack. The book he held open

26

to me, stroking the pages with his steady hand, the sound of skin on paper. His question so gently given up. – Which pages do you prefer in a book, he said: – When writing or reading, which do you prefer, the left or the right-hand pages?

And the question hung there – not that he forced a reply; he was not impatient. No. That was not his way; only the silence around us then, as if the volume had been turned down on those other gigglers slobbering outside the door, still queuing up for their five-minute buff. I answered very quietly. Heard myself speak, meaning to say the opposite, instead, hearing myself betray everything by announcing – The left … Left. Not a lie – worse. Because now I couldn't take it back. I couldn't tell him I'd made a mistake, gone in the wrong direction with the weight of the question, a mistake at the heart of hesitation, an inkling for the word left when I knew it was always the thickness, the reassurance, the promise, the headway of those right-hand sides I was after; everything the left could not give on opening a book. Everything they would become of course over time as pages reverse, replace, the right-hand pages turned and turned again becoming left, overwriting, over-reading, overturning, over time, at last, finishing. While all this was wanting in me, waiting to be said, I said nothing. Nothing more. Instead he spoke without looking at me. I watched his hand stroke the book, cover and smooth that chosen side with such love, such care. His side, my side, his proximity, his body not reacting to anything I'd said. – For me, he said, it is always the right-hand pages… The most pleasurable right. It was the word we shared – pleasure – the one I used quietly to myself even then at the age of twelve, what pleasure those pages gave me. Me too, I wanted to shout. But the moment had gone and it would have sounded foolish to retract, to change direction; never could I tell him what I had considered so many times in a short life, while dreaming and writing and reading, and smoothing open a book.

For we were not destined, Michael and me, to share any other play or role or friendship – only this one small moment where I could not change things, where I could not know how things might have changed between us, if only I could have said what I meant to … how I love those right-hand pages.

In the gold room, while everyone sleeps, I write to you. To whom are you writing you might ask if you were here? You I'd reply. Good, you'd say. Good.

The swallows are everywhere: lined up on the balcony beyond the tall windows in the gold room, squeezing themselves inside cracks in the walls of the square, swooping down and fighting over the bread baskets left on the café tables where En and me sit and drink coffee early mornings. The birds we called the secretary birds on account of the way they sound – as if they are typing at the end of a call, throwing their calls in the way a typewriter is pushed back to work the next line, the ting of the bell while the birds move on. The sky here seems bigger, we say in unison. The church bells call people to mass. We order more strong coffee. En reads Thomas Mann, and lost somewhere on a magic mountain he gradually begins to forget the letter, while I begin my own version. En is instead taking the air and the water of another time and country, falling in love with more than one fictional woman as I watch him read. Inside my empty coffee cup, a fat heart.

Dear ...

I find myself writing this down to address you, to form a reply. Dear ... so carefully written at the top of the page, left-hand side – the way I so faithfully learned in school. Nothing follows. With no name I falter. No need for Sir, not here ... Unless you are to become dearer to me than I can ever imagine. Dear to me in the true sense of the word. *For dear life.* To ask: anon ... what is Dear between us.

Dear ... *Used in direct address, especially in salutations.*
The rules of engagement
Ending sincerely
The aim
To be as sincere in my address to you as is possible.
Dear ...
To be regarded with much tenderness
My beloved, darling, loved one
My dearest wish is to send you word
Dear ...
At a high cost
Dear ...
A polite exclamation
Chiefly of surprise
Or distress
Oh dear, dear me

Dear Mr ...
I wish I could give you my name ...

This was how your letter opens, with a wish ... a wish for what cannot be given. Imagine instead if you'd changed your mind, granted the wish – like in the Panto when the fairy comes on, in her hair a small paste crown we want to believe is real – we want to believe that the fairy-dust is a magic potion she scatters as our eyes open wide in wonder - a tiny explosion a puff of smoke soon follows and voilà …

The name appears …

Who should I say called …

A name would have allowed a different kind of conversation. A name would have given a face, a body, a smile; a set of teeth could have inspired a completely different tête-à-tête. Names chained together like paper dolls, our names holding hands. A name would have allowed so much we are denied here in anonymity.

We all begin nameless.

Yes, when I was born I remained nameless for three days.

I have told this story many times. Mother wanting to name me Deborah, meaning 'bee': *a fiery spirit*. But Mother, numb with pushing, said I looked nothing like the Deborah she'd been expecting. Deborah never arrived. Deborah remained somewhere still inside my mother: shrivelled with the wait for the final heave. A nameless creature was pushed out instead. A nameless creature refusing to eat, eyes closed – knowing something wasn't right. On the third day one eye tentatively opened, so the story goes – in this rendition it is not specified if it was the right or the left eye that took the risk. My father, maybe out of desperation, named me after a TV game-show hostess he liked at the time. Years later, En renamed me Myrtle after a myrtle bush we'd planted in the whitewashed back yard, and after a rather feisty character in one of the cowboy films he was partial to watching on Sunday afternoons: Myrtle.

Myrtus: meaning love.

Myrtle becomes Mert – and over the years – Mort – Mertie.

Derivatives: appellation, sobriquet, tag, first-given alias; a tap of recognition under the chin.

After the news of your letter,

we all gathered around the kitchen table where it became normal to talk about the threat. To begin with, we talked about little else: with friends who phoned us, work colleagues, acquaintances, the man in the fish market, the waiters in the restaurant. Some listened more than others. Some shied away from bad news. Some didn't know how to take your words and said nothing, only examined their feet or changed the subject. Some floundered, got embarrassed, scared for us, or sometimes for themselves. Some said – What did you do to get a letter like this? – then they laughed. Jokes get people through, but there's always the slight gagging worry that's how others might see it, the *What did you do? ...*

After your letter arrived in our home, people began telling me their own stories: threats of violence, bullying, intimidation, the hurtful things people did or didn't do to others, as adults, as children, small acts of being bullied and bullying, things both given and received – making me think of all the things I'd witnessed when I was working in those huge psychiatric hospitals, only just eighteen years of age, things I hadn't thought of since, things I'd seen and spoke little of, the levels of threats and hurt that all institutions carry.

Our kitchen filled with the sounds of the kettle's whistle and other people's stories, while we speculated, dissected, mulled and stirred our tea around your threat. A threat that now, a year later, we rarely mention any more. Months on, a year on, where are we any longer in time, time snatched when your letter arrived, time now moving us forward, taking me back to a beginning where we forget so much, where so much is put away, compartmentalised, times change, events take over, distract us, ease us, without our noticing, routines return, the comfort of our day-to-day back in place when at the time there was only the impulse to try to tell you everything. There are always sides. I'll try to go on.

Yes, when your letter arrives people begin sharing their stories with me. Some were similar – letters, absurd renditions, written signs, letters that led to stalking, stolen letters, love letters, misunderstood, ignored letters – some of which I will share later. Others were much more extreme – accounts of actual bodily harm, acts I decided not to repeat, threats carried through, rape, murders, a sharp knife – back to that, the knife in the belly. Not that I am trying to set up hierarchies between violence that is written, verbalised, left to the imagination, as opposed to threats that are acted out, that in some cases kill the body. No; it was more a gradual acknowledgement of the difference between a body that is actually harmed, touched, killed by more than words, or how the violence of words alone can affect the body, anticipation that leaves the imagination open to who knows what ends, our fear of the stranger, the neighbour we don't know, the person we pass by, the anonymous other who calls out our name, calls out *You!*

That's the hard part, you see, when someone writes you a letter like this. The call to respond is such an old command, Pavlovian, the hand waving in the air, the phone ringing, the door bell, the scream called down the road, a letter stating *It's you I'm after, you …* Well, maybe not that simple; there's hesitation of course, but for sure within that hesitation there's my body set to respond, to move, to burst into action, a flutter of the heart, a flip of the stomach, a tensing of muscles, a grin or a grimace, the knees prepare themselves. Somewhere in me is that impulse to come back with something, some little nod, wink, toot the toot, a doffed cap, a curtsey and courtesy to answer. We all have our blind spots, our myopia and tendency to daydream. Yes, there I am scribbling in my notebook, laughing at the nonsense I wrote down: *When your letter arrived I can say it was as if Death had come pushing its nose to the house. That it skulked around the garden. Stood on boxes to peer inside the window, breathed condensation over the glass.*

You see who you wrote to? You see the kind of home you have entered? My sense of the theatrical that powers the picture house; the fight or flight of the imagination that threats rely on. When Death comes calling in those back yards and dank corners, points a finger and says ...

I choose you.

That simple ...

This blush, this shame ...

Select

To carefully choose as being the best or most suitable.

Select for or against survival ... or so it says in the big Dic.

The shy smile ...

The sorry.

Sorry!

You hear that all the time: in response to an accusation, a threat, the bump of someone's shoulder against yours, someone drops something, spills something, shuts a door in your face, and you hear yourself say *sorry* ahead of the other, even when you've done nothing wrong, here it comes, a hand so swiftly raised, yes, it was me. Guilty as charged. To point blameful fingers back at ourselves, the self-reproach waiting in us, the hair shirt, the defence, armaments, or is that *amour*ments, the sandbags dragged to the door, the face burning up, the dry palms, the garrulousness ... all of it an apology, to say in response to the eye on you that the body remembers these old commands, even if the will says No. The body remembers what we cannot.

Yes, when someone writes you a letter like this, a corker, a whopper with extra cheese – your instinct – among others – is to write back, to want to speak – with you; to you; *you and no body else will do.* I hear the call, the whistle, find myself wanting to tell you my side, our side, backside – even if words fail and fall on shallow fallow soil, no soil, no one's listening – no one's gardening, no one's pulling up a chair or mowing the lawn or trimming the wicks – there's only the sound of my own spit and polish, the sound of me trying to keep going with you, the sound of me waking at night composing sentences to you, the sound of my own desire, worry, need to tell you, to let you know …

En's account of receiving the letter.

When I received the letter I was in work at The Quad and even though I was not expecting it at all, I understood what it was straight away. Obviously I felt that my body was under threat because when someone threatens to do you harm, that usually means something physical, but when I received the letter, the bit that I felt had been invaded wasn't my body, it was more an invasion of you, the kids, our home. It's always been really important to me that my home life and my work life are kept completely separate, but what happened was there were people threatening me who knew where I lived and I didn't know if they would come to the house and what they might do to you and the kids; even though they'd said you and the kids would be OK, that it was me they would hurt, you can never be sure of anything when something like that happens. I didn't know where or who or when something would happen or what would happen and that not knowing made the whole thing feel – well, it's just that you can't compartmentalise the threat because the threat is everywhere – any time, anywhere, someone could take their opportunity to hurt you.

I didn't know how I was supposed to act. I didn't know what the threat was, apart from the word hurt, which can mean anything, can't it. And the fact that they said it would be a delayed threat, when I least expected it, when I thought I was OK and was beginning to feel safe; so I thought that it could happen at any time, at the time of receiving the letter or at any time in the future. I was obviously expecting it at any time, but also the placing of it into a future tense, to come, when I least expected it, made it worse. I didn't know if it was someone in work, not in work, someone who could have paid someone to do something to me, or get someone to do it as a favour to them, or maybe someone who was a bit unhinged. People felt sure

35

from the language and the way that the letter was worded and constructed that it was a professional educated person trying to sound the opposite. Despite this, there was no evaluation of what was going on, or where the threat was going to come from. It was impossible to compartmentalise the danger or the risk and view all of it, deal with it, as I didn't know what I was going to have to deal with because it just came anonymously and out of the blue. Even though I took advice from all these different people at work who gave me tips about my safety: where to park the car, changing my route home; The Quad even suggested that I have someone follow me home, told me to check under my car each day, insisted that others should escort me to meetings I had to attend outside of the main building. But finally, if the person or persons knew where I lived, as they had said that in the letter, then the threat was there all the time, not just during work, or on the way home, or to and from work, but after work, at the weekends, any time.

I couldn't respond to the threat because I had no idea who had made the threat and so I suppose in some way that's why I really wanted my employers to put something out in the press because that way it would reach the person, because in the letter they'd already mentioned the press and that they'd be looking out in the newspapers to see if anything had changed regarding the decision. I can't really say too much about the reason why they were threatening me because I can't breach confidentiality. It was linked to a decision made at work to disband a specialist team, and the person who wrote the letter said they had been saved by this particular team. Everyone who read the letter said it was written by someone posing as an ex-client, someone who had an interest in things staying as they were. We can never know for sure. All that was certain was that they wanted the decision to be overturned and didn't want any changes to happen. What I wanted The Quad to do

36

was to separate me from that decision – not to say that these changes may not happen but to say that it wasn't me who was responsible, separate that link between the thing that wound the person up, and the fact that they were associating it with me – but of course they were not prepared to do that in the press, to make a clear statement. The Quad became part of the problem. I didn't feel that straight away, but gradually came to realise it, which is ultimately why I left and stopped working there as it felt that the only way to separate myself from the threat was to get away from the source of it and the source of it was work.

We make assumptions about our safety, that we are free to walk around and that nothing will happen to us, and then there was this person saying that you no longer could trust that or take it for granted. I found the language in the letter quite disturbing, the personal insults about me being short, for instance, and the thought of somebody out there having such hateful feelings that they'd sit down and write me a letter like that. Of course, maybe it was more that they were being calculating, a means to change things, or rather wanting things to stay as they were. But whatever their reasons, the effects of their personal attacks and language were still the same.

As the person receiving the letter, it is not possible to get into the mind of the person who has written the threat, yet everyone tries to do that – the police, The Quad… We had loads of conversations about what sort of person this could be. Trying to analyse, people said things like, *Oh, people who want to really hurt you don't make threats, they just do it,* but you can't know that. I think it's dangerous to try to get into the psychology behind it – you just don't know, do you. And in the end it's not just the person who wrote the letter, it's everyone knowing about the letter, people talking about it, your name associated with it, and that's difficult. Imagine how certain public figures feel, the number of threats they must get.

I didn't think I had accepted that kind of risk when I'd agreed to do that job. I realise that making hard decisions is part of the job, but there is a decision-making process that's collective and we all played our part. I wasn't the one who made the final decision, nor was I the one who authorised that decision. That was for other people to make. I was instructed that I had to cut services, had to make savings – and I think about that even now, even now in my current job we are going through similar things, having to cut back on services, close services, and I think yes, we have to do this and that, and then I think, hang on a minute, what the fuck! Soon I could end up having a load of angry people start something threatening all over again – but at least I now live miles away from work, and I remember at the time knowing that the people responsible for writing that letter maybe lived near our house, had identified where we lived, and that made it worse.

If I'd thought that a real threat was coming at me from a certain person I might have been prepared to do something to them or get someone else to do something. I did think about it – not as a strategy, more a fantasy, about finding out who this person was and really beating them because of what they did to me, and to you as well, when they wrote that letter. I don't know if I would have acted this out, because I am not a violent person, but I visualised it. It's not a solution, because in the end it could have just made matters worse. I could have lost my job or ended up in prison or something like that and it certainly isn't rational – but at the time you just want to separate yourself from the threat in whatever way you can and to put it back where it came from. The other side of it was that there were people I knew who I suspected were involved in one way or another. Of course I didn't know for sure, I couldn't have known if they wrote the threat letter, but I certainly knew that they were angry with me about the decision and I do remember having really powerful feelings of hatred towards them at the time.

When I thought about the threat, I used to imagine two or three people just stopping me in the street and beating me, putting a knife through me, or hitting me with sticks or clubs, kicking me or whatever – that's what you imagine when people say they are going to hurt you or put a stop to your comfortable life or whatever they said, you know – you imagine having your legs broken or your arms broken. It hadn't been that long before that a client at work, because we were challenging something he had done, threatened to come to The Quad with a pickaxe handle and break my arms. I'd already had that threat, and in that instance the guy had completely lost it, but I knew who he was and where he lived and so the police were able to go around and deal with it and that was the end of it. That contained the violence, or rather the threat. Having an anonymous letter and not knowing where it originated, having suspicions, makes it worse.

For all I knew, one of the people I thought might have written the letter could have been in the room when I opened it at The Quad. At the time I hadn't made a connection. In retrospect that could have been part of the thing, them being there to witness my distress when I opened the letter, my humiliation. I'm not sure, but after I left The Quad the decision to disband the team did go ahead without me even being there, and so in a way everybody lost out, everyone was affected, lots of people's lives were made unhappy because of what happened – apart from the institution, that is. The Quad was never touched, it goes on, people are dispensable and get replaced, come and go and the machine goes on regardless, they just do what they can to cover their own arses, do everything they can possibly do to satisfy themselves that they are covering their own corner, and that nobody can blame them, nothing can come back at them.

At the time, for my safety, I was off work. Some people were of course genuinely caring, I know that, and others purporting to be but really just trying to be seen to be doing their jobs well, ensuring they were protecting me, and our home. By the end of a few weeks they were really anxious to get me back, and they needed me back because there was always so much work that needed to be done. Before I could return a lot of bargaining went on – a whole list of conditions and plans for my safety were drawn up and they all had to agree to make sure we were safe at home and at work. But making sure we were safe at home was in many ways impossible; alarms could only do so much. When something like this happens in a work setting, it all gets focused too much on the person who has received the threat; it makes it personal, when it isn't. Well, the person who writes the letter makes it this way when it really shouldn't have been aimed at one person. But from the letter-writer's perspective, how do you attack such a huge faceless organisation, where do you start if you're not happy with changes being proposed? So the person making the threat personalised it, when what happened came from a decision taken by The Quad about budget cuts. The way the decision was leaked to the press fuelled a lot of anger.

In the beginning you have the support of work and some notoriety. I got a pass to the underground car park. That makes me laugh! There are always perks, and I don't mean the alarms we had to have in the house and things like that. Looking back, the most absurd thing that happened as a result of the letter was those two women turning up with their power tools to attach the letterbox with a fire extinguisher inside. That was probably the highlight of the whole thing, the absurd image of them drilling our door.

I don't think about any of this much any more, not really, only occasionally. For instance, earlier today, when I was walking into town on my own, a man waved at me, a stranger, someone just wandering around near where we live, and maybe he was just being friendly, might just be a coincidence, but it made me think about it again. You don't normally think about the strangers you encounter, but that's what the letter had implied, that the person knew where we lived and so walking around certain areas near here made me see people differently, worry more.

I don't think any of The Quad policies have changed or even been looked at as a result of what happened to me. It is very common for people working there and in similar jobs to get threats – death threats even, some explicit. At one time several people who instigated a decision to close a particular centre were sent written death threats. They never spoke to me about it. I only found out about it after I got my own letter and people in The Quad began talking about how common it is.

There was a man today running through the vegetables. Running in great haste. I could not make out whether they were cabbages, the beginnings or the ends of something, close to the ground, the vegetables between tall stalks. He ran between the rows of things he might have once planted; furrowed brow and earth, his head as if pulled along, *arrastrado*; old-cardiganed again; sagging arse and old flesh. It hurts to see an old man run that way. Fleeing, or was he after something? Was he frightened or was he running towards something he had forgotten or not fully known or thought through yet? He did not fall. – Our hearts are not made like artichokes or onions, someone said while we watched him run. We have to make do.

En sweeping again like a good señora, like our Greek neighbour back home, like the aproned ladies who sweep their fronts each day, bleach their stones. En sweeps the remnants of last night's birthday party for our son Hugo. We lit candles outside. Last night we played a subversive form of 'I Spy', using more than one sense, making no-sense, double- and triple-barrelled clues that ended in five or more words. To guess: MGM, *Mert's glorious menopause*, TSOC, *the sound of crickets*, TTAFEIC, *two thousand and four etched into cement*. TRHPTGATSMASOLP, *the random harvester passes the gate at the same moment a strange old lady passes*. The last one was just impossible and kept us there for over an hour.

Remember that day a plaque on a synagogue, but spelled with a *sin* in Spanish, the SIN highlighted in gold paint, carefully. We forgot to make a clue from this. And from Julian, the waiter, *Junta* as Hugo called him, kissing me on both cheeks, his adult teeth stained with tobacco, as tiny as milk-teeth.

I spy a demented woman in the doorway – a perfect strawberry bob, floral frock – she stares at us. She stares and her daughter suddenly remembers her, squeezes her arms, rotates her, eyes front, leads her back up the steps of the small bar, where she then stands still – and still stares at us while licking an ice-cream. The tongue whips up what cannot be remembered.

On the way to the Mountain of the Dead Woman we stopped over at the Museum of the Angels, transformed from an old flour mill. Inside we stared at the figure of an angel on the wall, carved from wood, legs apart – a new angel born from this angel's open thighs, wings wet with afterbirth, a different shade of wood. She averted her eyes to heaven. She was far away, the angel giving birth to an angel; like the woman eating ice-cream, she was entranced. – If there's a heaven, D said – which there isn't, but if there is, I'd like to believe it looks like this place and is a flour mill; that God wears a striped pinny and leaves his trace in self-raising.

Feathers floated everywhere. There were even feathers in a fire bucket mixed with sand and dog-ends. A stray feather floated along the floor. We looked around but could not find the source of them. Only through the open window the sound of something being slaughtered in the neighbouring fields. Outside the window shoes hung from a clothesline in the sun, the sun so bright it obliterated the line and so all you could see were shoes suspended, walking on air. *Windows*, my abandoned book; daily conversations between us about weather and washing and how one affects the other. En reminding Luke of how he once – for a joke, he added – hung him from a washing-line by his fingers and let go. – Tiny babies have a natural grip, he said.

– Naturally I knew not to let go, Luke said.

– Naturally I was ready to catch you if you fell.

There are times when, forty or more pages in – so many words between us already – I begin to wonder about the tone of my voice.

How to speak with you, how to find the right way, lippy starts, a tuning fork held to the ear. No need for sarcasm but maybe it's only normal that a little seeps out, not intended but maybe inevitable here and there. I had no intentions when I set off to write to you – to begin with I meant only to reply – to riposte, come back, counter, sally, not so fast, not so much of a thrust as an amble around you. I admit that I have no way of knowing how to approach. And there are times like now when I catch myself unexpectedly, seeing myself so verbose, so far into my flurry, so deeply lost in words to you, digressions to you, little stories coming and going, coming and going, that I begin to wonder if I am adopting the right sound. Yes, I could say it occurs to me each time I embark on a new work: whatever small things I may find myself engrossed in, there's always concern over the voice that will emerge …

Which reminds me of a time when I was writing to a friend. A piece about digressions, about memory and digression, and we were digressing well enough and remembering what we could drag up – yes, we were deep into our discourse. My reply to him was extensive, his reply to me woven between. We kept adding and subtracting – I was never good at maths, but here we were adding and subtracting between each other's words, and then after some time, many words in, but in an instant, I realised that I had the tone all wrong. The voice I'd imagined as teasing – fooling around, although tender – yes, I meant him no harm – ha … back to that! – I found that, after some pages of what I had imagined was a playful reply, I didn't like the tone I found myself using – if one can see that far back from the tone one is using.

44

But to return... I had been writing to a friend once, found myself deep into my reply, fingers freely zipping along the keyboard, when suddenly the voice on the page made me hesitate, caused me to stop writing, to abandon all we had said, to want to delete, to wipe clean, to take a sop and rag and Windolene to it all, to call out *Stop*, to admit that I did not like who I had become in those few pages. Already becoming a character I was struggling to relate to, too much a brand. I told my friend that as I wrote I could see myself in mink – mink! Yes, maybe I should start again. – Let's go back, I said. – No, he said, let's go on for a minute ... let's digress into mink. – OK ... I can see myself in mink, in mink that looks cheap; my hair is dyed badly and I don't like my shade of lipstick and my nails are chipped and I'm beginning to look like Tippy: Tippy in Hitchcock's *The Birds*. Yes, Tippy just came into my head. – Amazing, the way the mind deviates from blushes to mink in just a few lines, he said.

And who can stop these things coming and going. These things that move inside me all the time when then, as now, I set out so composed, so ready to tell you some small stories, to give you some insight into how it was for us to be on the other side of your words, some little tattle and cup of sugar over the fence and now here as then, I was and am already lost. Yes, there I was writing to my friend, completely lost in Tippy's white mink, in her tight-assed green suit – imagine: what a way to dress to speak with someone. A voice emanating from a tight green suit – though a very unusual shade of green, a yellow-green, a difficult-to-place green, but classic. Not a colour you'd find in any old High Street, rather a very distinctive shade that complements her hair and skin. Tippy has money, she has style, she has danced in fountains of Rome naked – or so the story goes. She denied it, of course, and had that little tantrum with Mitch – but it only made her more adorable – that little stamp

45

of the foot, that little twist of the lip, the way she drives off so fast, trying to be angry – and of course Mitch just smiles back and sinks his hands into his pockets and he knows she is his: already that proves it, the little stamp of her foot, the roar of the car, she's lost, she's fucked, until later, much later, she ends up bandaged, stunned, her head bound like her body, bound in her now-bloodied suit, her chipped coral nail varnish indicating her violation, indicating ... Oops! ... And there I was, in danger of slipping from blushes to mink to cheap '70s feminist politics when I'd promised myself to give all that up years back, when I'd found myself with Tippy, yes, but more than that, when I'd noticed something – a little cock-a-hoop emerging, and I found myself wanting to tell the friend I was writing to about the way Tippy held and smoked a cigarette, the way she tried to run in her tight skirt, the way she tried to assert herself unsuccessfully with her handbag, making it through every drama. – A girl is nothing without her handbag, I told him, but maybe that was only further milking the ash blonde voice making its ascent from my throat.

And all this came back to me, when I found myself wondering how to talk with you, how to tell you something about myself, about the family, the lives you entered with your letter. Anonymity aside, we'd worked over the *Dear* enough, no need to go on with that – so the *how* now began to bother me... No longer a question of *if* I should write to you – we had come too far for *if*s. I was already many pages in and committed to you wholeheartedly, pledged, bound, dedicated, '*with You*' ... Yes, it was no longer a question of *should I write to you*, imprison myself to the machine over you, no longer *if* but *how*: how to be with you, how to write this to you without sounding too this or too that... A love letter of sorts, I'd told someone – *what saccharine notions*. Luke, yes, it was Luke I began telling, way back when I started those first pages in a small insignificant village on the edge of a mountain in Spain. I had been explaining to Luke – blathering on, no doubt, with no idea what I was saying – that my impulse to write to you did not come out of anger, or malice – well, maybe a little anger – the type that comes from protection – cannot, should not be denied here – but I hoped to go beyond that, hoped that the writing would lead to some understanding, to counteract whatever harm had been pressed into the pages between us; that my response, however flawed, might end in a kiss … Luke questioned. I blushed. I blushed at the thought of you. We can sometimes stray so far from those early gestures once we set off to write. Voices calling beside the coincidence of those lyrics of love Luke had so wanted to write while we were away.

– Love songs, not so far away from harm, a friend had said.

Sarah sending me little songs in response to all I had told her of my letter to you; love letter, love song, little lyrics, – I'm not one for binaries, she said, but love/hate can come out the same. Remember Sting, she said … *Every step you take, every move you make … I'll be watching you …*

– Can't you write about love instead, my father says, a sweet little love story.

Maybe I am, I tell him. *Every letter is a love letter*, Kraus says.

Every Letter is a Love Letter …

Encounter, both to meet and to struggle with, confront, face, faceless your words instead became the missing face I read. To translate your absent lips. I write, to you, despite you; denied a name, an address, still I hear my voice, conscious that it directly addresses you just so. And maybe that's all I can hope for, that the colour of my suit is of no concern, that the tone I use must be earned over time, over days, with patience, with the volume of words, with my commitment to you. Yes, maybe over time I will put away the mink, hang up the green

47

of Tippy's suit, a blonde wig exchanged for one endless letter unfolding itself as a hand reaches over the large expanse of landscape between us, from Spain to home, from me to you, from here to there. You and I pressed into words, into the rag and weave and watermark of paper. You are somewhere out there. I write you. Make you up, writing on a marble table in a café among strangers, experiencing the kindest and the cruellest of lines, small gestures, scratched-out frustration – witness my misspelling, impatience, my inability to articulate – see how flawed I can be, how tedious, how repetitive. My circling hand cramps from writing too quickly, ahead of myself, language moving back in time. I become démodé. I dispense my words to you. Words intimately folded inside my book, closed only to be opened. Words wrapped to be unwrapped. Yes, if I were to post these words to you, if there was an envelope, many envelopes, if there was a seal, to deliver myself to you, my final gesture would be to salivate.

Let me come to the point

I never saw an envelope. The one the letter arrived in, that is. I presume brown. No saliva. That's what they said, the police: that the envelope had one of those self-adhesive seams – no need to lick, neither the envelope nor the stamp. You couldn't go through with spit. Not a trace, they said, and this made me suspicious when maybe I have no right to be, imagine! The closeness of your tongue on a glued edge, a paper-cut to the tongue, sharp as the letter. Paper-cuts, they seem like nothing, they seem too small even to mention, not technically a cut at all, those little hoodlums that hurt the most – we all know that. I understand the precaution over saliva. Your choice of envelope – I would have done the same, unless I do you an injustice and that's all that was to hand, self-adhesion leaving you with no

48

choice but to put your tongue back in your mouth. The lack of DNA – or so they say, the police, when they call around, after some time. Around the same time, a woman detective is assigned to the case. She seems more mature and intelligent than the rest. She apologises and seems to have more of an understanding of the fear, however irrational, that the letter brings. She drinks her tea without milk and eats one biscuit, as she is watching her weight. She sets up a date for En to make an official statement at the station where he will also have his elimination prints taken. That's what they called them: *To differentiate between the fingerprints of the regular residents and unwanted visitors.* And then to eliminate the people at The Quad. The obvious others: the post room workers, the secretaries, the delivery boys, people who looked the letter over, innocent enough, all those who passed it around to read and re-read to one another. No one thought to wear gloves, everyone handling it like that, the lack of evidence, your prints maybe among them – unless you wore gloves, someone saying, you must have worn gloves. What type of glove, no one specified: white cotton, oven gloves, winter mitts, the wife's velvet evening gloves. (As usual I go too far …) The policewoman reiterates that it is not common for anything to come from a letter like this; that it is probably a 'one-off'. More police call around. They eat biscuits, some more than others. They repeat what she said. It's part of the torch race – often dry rendition, rarely rococo.

One evening we take a stroll to the police station, and surely we look to fellow amblers as if we are just out for an evening's jaunt through the park – the same route as I regularly take to the museum. Carried on the warm air: the sounds of a circus being set up, people arm-in-arm or walking dogs, children pushed in various forms of carriage – a merry scene. Imagine us all, walking past each other with no idea of where everyone else is headed. Imagine the destinations, if we took the time and the risk to stop and ask. Imagine the wide tales, the yarns, and a woman on a bench with a beard. I swear, officer! I saw her on the way here. Only I'll say nothing. These days I do not talk to or take anything from strangers – except the odd glance and smiles we cannot stop coming our way.

Imagine if the bearded lady were you. I see things like this and wonder if I am making her up, but she does smile at me, as if she knows something of our destination. This is how I am – making it all up, telling myself that people know where we are headed. I am sure I notice that her beard is very strong, white – not like Santa, not a soft beard, not fluffy like a candyfloss, but stiff white hairs sprouting from a lived-in face, a face neglected but not aware of it. I want to ask her if I can help relieve her of the hair, to clip and lovingly cream it clean away, but she is smiling and seems totally at ease. All this in a week when someone had shown me an image of a bearded lady, someone she found, an artist maybe, a writer; I forget so much, but the coincidence of the image passed around the table. The woman in the image was beautiful: the beard black tight curled neat around her chin. The woman in the park is not in any way groomed; maybe it is my own concern causing me to assume the hair is unwanted, rough to the touch; that it has surely taken a year or more to reach this length is a presumed sign of isolation – what is she doing on this bench bearded and smiling at me ... I do not touch, or know, or approach, nor do I like to point her out to En, who at the time is watching the Big Top as it is spread out over the fields. I will forget to mention her to the woman who passed around the photograph of the bearded lady only days back, even though the lady who had the photograph has taken to writing me beautiful letters, saying at the end of the last one ... *I have a habit of writing more letters than I send; apparently this is a woman's thing, but I promise to start sending them to you ...* She also writes, *I write better lying down.* – Me too, I want to reply, back to the bed. Asking – *Do you ever run from your words, even when lying down, or even know you are running, or do you face them like Goliath, like a man* – or like a bearded lady? I forget to ask the woman who writes me letters the name of the bearded lady in the image. I will not ask the lady on the bench her name. I will not ask her anything, or explain the coincidence of seeing two bearded ladies in the space of mere days. I will take her smile and it will remain, her smile, her beard – will she know this, that I will now carry her with me, tell others, this fleeting moment; this anonymous stranger who is not you.

We are going to the Station – I haven't forgotten our destination, why we are in the park this evening; I want to tell the bearded lady we are on our way, and not to the train. I make no connection at the time between her and the circus. I am holding En's hand – one of the hands that are on their way to be fingerprinted. Elimination prints, they call them, and again the word is repeated as if to reinforce his innocence. He is not under suspicion but he is holding my hand. While we wait in the police station reception, two young women make a dramatic entrance, out of breath, red-faced, talking over each other, reporting an assault, saying that two men had approached them, that it had ended in threats to beat them … We are invited inside to an interview room just as they are beginning to detail who said and did what, and so we miss the end of their story. The policeman explains that if I am to stay in the room while En makes a written statement – and has his elimination prints taken – I am not allowed to say a word or to give any kind of nonverbal cue that could influence his account of things. He apologises for the delay in getting this written down, sorted out.

On the wall there's a large whiteboard full of red arrows and green lines, wild circles of yellow, a map of names that outlines an unnamed crime. Like those maps you see on TV, on cop shows like *Prime Suspect*. 'Orange Trainer Man', it reads, 'MT arrested, PH under suspicion.' Arrested, arrested, resisting arrest. Missing. Last seen. Alias. Blue Pinstripe Man, Red Plastic Bag Woman, Little White Dog Boy. No one has seen the bearded lady. I hear En retell his story. I want to add things but maintain the agreed silence. The story told and retold will begin to sound as delicate, as make-believe, as the sight of a policeman finally taking En's hands in his, guiding him around the table as if to a sink, wiping each hand with a small alcohol wipe as carefully as a mother would wash her child after a hard day at play. The policeman who wipes explains that the elimination prints will be compared to other fingerprints that are recovered from the letter and envelope. These prints, he tells us, will be compared to others by ridges and a number of identifying marks; the prints will be dusted with aluminium powder to enhance them. I enjoy the word *aluminium* but don't mention it, forgetting that I am no longer sworn to muteness. He says, these fingerprints will then be destroyed. I want to say that I would like to keep them, to ask if they could please be sent home to me. Home. En's prints, but who could utter such a need. I watch the policeman roll each of En's fingers onto a pad of Indian ink, then press and roll each finger onto paper as if he were rolling tiny rugelach pastries. We start with the finger, he says, rolling it like this, from left round to the right so that you get a complete print. When you look at the actual fingerprint, he says, it is almost twice the size of your finger. This is because the whole finger has been rolled from side to side. The thumbprint is made by simply pushing the centre of the thumb into the ink for printing, like this; feel the pressure on the nail of the thumb, blood momentarily trapped. Then the palm pressed hard, like this.

He uses a roller loaded with ink, pushing down En's palm onto paper. This leaves a clear print. He says: – Look, one, two. Like the prints D and Hugo brought home from school, way back, powder-blue prints repeated. Or like the painted face of the child killer Myra Hindley made up of dozens of tiny child's handprints. Lifeline, brain line, destiny, the lines of the heart, arch, loop, whorl, bulb of the thumb, first joint – I peep across at the black patterns that are left. While this is going on, the officer's wife rings several times and asks him what he wants for dinner, just as En and me would talk when he was at work at The Quad. They discuss hot curried meat, rice and two types of green veg, or whether for ease they should go for a cold chicken salad. My mouth, still forbidden to speak, can salivate. The policeman tells her not to worry, explaining that he'll be a little delayed. – Fifty minutes, darling, and I'll be home. The sound of *darling* runs around the room, brings a new name to the whiteboard: the chicken salad is innocent, and darling man's on the run. He apologises, tells us that she worries and he hopes we don't mind him taking care of the call. *Taking care of a call.* I love that, but I don't say so.

Seeing that everything is now being tidied away, I break my curfew to say that I'd heard that there were special procedures for fingerprinting people who have extra fingers, or amputations, webbed fingers, split thumbs. He seems a little embarrassed and it's hard to tell if this is in response to the call, or to the absurdity of my question, or the sudden guest appearance of my voice. He agrees that there are special procedures but that he's never come across such a situation in all the time he's been taking prints – maybe the odd bandage and scar, but no more than that. He hands me a small chart of techniques on reading fingerprints. *Basic and composite ridge characteristics (minutiae)* it says. *Crossover. Core. Bifurcation. Ridge ending. Island. Delta. Pore.* Tint prints that look like the swirl at the tip of a head of short hair, or furrowed land – yes, like seeing the earth from the sky, from satellite, *lake, hook, spur, bridge.* En's fingertips framed like tiny woodcuts.

~

…For now I have no notion what to call this reply – by definition, I mean: no way of categorization, either fictionally or in terms of any category of letter or misdemeanour. What to call these words to you? Your words to En, everyone reaching for the inevitable *threat*, the word *threat* examined sometime later in a book, a rather cheap book I found, *self-help*, it said, the sort of book that you can buy beside the tomatoes and condoms at the supermarket, the type of book that comes with a title in oversized gold letters, a book that I came across in an attempt to understand what others were saying on the subject, the subject of threats, verbal or written: *The Gift of Fear,* so-called, *and other survival signals that can protect us from violence. This book can save your life,* it read. *Number one national bestseller by Gavin de Becker.* A man Oprah Winfrey calls 'The nation's leading expert on violent behaviour…' The author states that *Every story in this book is true.*

He writes, *some violence, like any behaviour, has a purpose … If the person's desired outcome is to inflict physical injury, then there are few alternatives to violence. If a desired outcome is to punish someone, there might be many.*

…The threat means that at least for now, he has considered violence and decided against it …

Another tip: threateners often lose their will over time. Threats and promises alike are easy to speak, harder to honour. He gains advantage, [only] *through your uncertainty, but once the words are spoken, he must retreat or advance, and like all people, he hopes to retain dignity through either course … It is the listener and not the speaker who decides how powerful a threat will be. If the listener turns pale, starts shaking, and begs for forgiveness, he has turned the threat or intimidation into gold…*

Or a gold room.

The letter, is a case of … blackmail, some said. A public order offence, the two young police officers concluded over a chocolate finger, a fig roll, strong shots of coffee. Days later. Post-elimination prints. We were back around the old faithful kitchen table. A public order offence. Isn't that someone pissing on your strawberry patch, keeping you awake at night, stealing your milk? Others contradicted, little more was said. The categories are hard, they said, hard as a ginger nut on a set of false teeth. Still, we carry around the definition of blackmail on a small piece of paper – just in case we need to remember the wording… Nothing is confirmed. Someone from The Quad says, Crime doesn't pay. Cheats never prosper. No place like home…

A police account concerning threat letters

Threat letters have been sent to various members of the community since letter-writing began, whether royalty, government officials, police officers or heads of departments. Threats to cause psychological harm, threats to cause physical harm and threats to cause damage. The law in relation to threat letters covers quite a broad range. Threat letters constitute a form of harassment, but equally, if someone is sending a threat letter, making a demand with menaces upon somebody, then that would effectively become blackmail. In terms of the law, the offence of blackmail would be committed if the purpose of sending the letter was to make an unwarranted demand with menaces. To give you an example: if you get a letter from the local electricity board saying, *unless you pay your bill we are going to turn your lights off,* that's a demand for money with a threat, but is totally lawful. If the letter was rephrased saying: *if you don't pay the money we are going to come and knock your lights out,* that's a demand with menaces. The threat upon a person or person's stating, *if they don't do something then they will suffer harm,* be it psychological or physical: that is a criminal offence and will be investigated by the police.

The letter doesn't have to be received by the recipient to make it an offence. The minute the person types the letter and posts it, the offence is complete. Once it's in the post box and the letter is on its way, there is nothing that person can do. They can't wait for the postman to come the next day and empty the box and then take the letter back. Technically, the letter, once posted and until it is delivered, has become the property of the Royal Mail or other postal services. So the effect of making that threat, certainly for blackmail, is made at the point of posting. For harassment, on the other hand, where someone is causing alarm or distress to somebody, such as stalking-type scenarios, for that offence, the first occasion someone harasses another they would be given a warning about their conduct. If it happened again, then the offence is complete, although there are currently discussions about changing this law so that the arrest can occur on the first occasion. In terms of people receiving letters of threat, we would have to look at the content of the letter to establish whether that constitutes harassment or blackmail.

When a threat letter is received and enters the police system that letter is sealed in an envelope as evidence. From a procedural point of view, one of the first things that a police officer would look at would be to try to identify who the sender or the author of the letter was: is there a signature or a date and place from which it is sent. Clearly in the case of the letter En received there was no reference to anyone. If a letter is posted, it would have a frank on it; this mark can identify who owns that frank, the Post Office or a local company. You can pretty much source the area from which the letter was posted but of course that doesn't mean to say that the person who wrote the letter lives in that area – they could go anywhere to post it. You can then analyse the envelope for fingerprints and DNA. Even with a self-adhesive envelope, it's not uncommon for someone to lick it before realising, so it is still something you could swab and try and recover DNA from. It depends how anonymous the person wants to be. If forensically aware, they would wear gloves. They'd wear gloves when they were typing it, writing it, they'd wear gloves when they were sealing it, there would be no bodily contact between that letter, that envelope, and the person who was the author or the sender. But not everybody is forensically aware; or sometimes they think they are but they will slip up. If a letter has been dusted with aluminium dust to enhance a fingerprint and fingerprints are recovered, they are searched on the national database, and if that person has been in contact with the police at some stage previously and their fingerprints are on that database, then they can easily be eliminated from that inquiry or identified as a suspect.

It's not that often we get threat letters come through the post. Clearly the method by which most people communicate these days, apart from face-to-face communication and telephone, is email and text messaging. Email is more traceable in as much as you've got an email address, so that inquiries can be made to try and locate who that address belongs to, but even that can be difficult. Text messaging is slightly different, because a lot of people are on contract phones and there is an audit trail for all electronic communication. Do you remember the old days, when kidnap demands where sent in letters and the words were cut out from little pieces of newspapers? That was a really menacing way of making a demand on someone, or wishing to place a threat upon somebody, but those kinds of letters are now very few and far between. More threats are verbal as opposed to something that has been documented. Clearly when someone makes a threat, and wants to remain totally anonymous, then they are not going to want to physically see the person they are threatening, or give them any opportunity to say this was the accent, this sounded like the age of the person, or to know if the person were male or female. The letter's power is in its total anonymity.

In this particular case, the letter has been typed on an old-fashioned typewriter, and there are not too many of those about. And those that are, are not always in good working order and it is very hard to get hold of new ribbons for them. You could start by looking at who would have access to such a typewriter. I would say that is interesting, as the question for me would be, why is someone using this type of machine, what was their mindset when they were thinking of sending the letter, why did they think of using an old-fashioned typewriter, why not type it on a computer, print it out and send it. It seems strange nowadays that someone would use a manual typewriter to write a threat letter, when you could just go to an internet café or a library and type it on a computer. Pretty much most households now have got a computer, but the person who typed this letter was familiar with the traditional method of erasing spelling mistakes by overtyping with the XXXXX. One thing to look at when people are investigating this kind of letter would be to see if there were any typewriter letters missing or damaged.

I do have personal experience of threat letters that were received in relation to a family business – a very similar sort of thing to the letter En received. An anonymous letter with threats that stated, if you don't do this, then this will happen. So I know the impact on a family, the wider family, and how it affects your day-to-day life. I don't think you can ever say that any one threat letter could be compared with another one; it depends on the person receiving the letter and how they respond. The threat contained in a letter may seem nothing to one person but to another can be a really harrowing experience. Some threat letters talk about physical violence, targeting family members or children, these are very hard for people to deal with, especially when children are brought into it. When a person writes a letter to one individual and they keep it to themselves, then clearly that isn't going to have an impact on the wider family, but when the letter is shared with other family members, then that letter becomes a threat to everyone. The psychological trauma of receiving a letter can sometimes isolate that person from their family because they may not share their thoughts and feelings. The fear of intimidation to the rest of the family leaves them dealing with that threat on their own. Even if they do share some of what has happened, can the rest of the family honestly know how difficult it is for the person receiving the letter, what they are suffering? You cannot.

When you work for the police there is always an element where we become the bad guys, because we imprison or have had an impact on someone's liberty. Very often there are threats made against officers. If you are dealing with violent criminals, then there are always those who'll seek some kind of retribution for what you've done, even though you have acted within the law. Often it's just seen as part of the job – you accept that people are going to make threats. Any confrontation between you and another person can be intimidating. The day-to-day threats you get from people who in the heat of the moment say, *I'm going to come and burn your house down* – that often goes over your head. But serious threats, against your family, your home, you personally, your car – that is different. It has an impact on you, depending what line of work you are in and what kind of criminals you are dealing with. In a previous role I was surveilled from work. There are those who want to know where you live, what type of car you drive. They will sit outside the police station and wait for you to leave. It wasn't uncommon to leave the office and notice that a very short distance away, the same car was behind you. So you do what you can to avoid this, take some sort of evasive action. I'd have to leave work from different exits, leave at different times of the day, and vary my route home. But no matter what kind of evasive action you take to avoid them knowing where you live, it is so easy these days to find out. So much information is freely available; you can easily track anyone down. I was thinking of that last night in terms of the Google street map, where you can pretty much see into people's living rooms.

Why only you now why...

The night of the letter, night one, I had a dream which became a recurring dream thereafter. A dream where – don't laugh – Cary Grant appeared as Death. Although I think that when I woke I'd called him God. An easy mistake, but don't get me wrong: he had charisma. He was Cary Grant, for God's sake. Who could be more charming. Maybe that's why I got him mixed up with God. It can happen – God, Death – who could know. Anyway, in the dream Cary-as-Death or -as-God, depending on your preference for dream interpretation – personally I try not to interpret the night's slumber; I try just to enjoy the images, and a good yawn – he wore a very gorgeous suit, Cary-as-Death or -God. A well-cut blue-grey suit, good cloth. And in the dream he woke me. In the dream I was in a king-size bed at one end of the room, and he was in a chair, a very comfortable deep armchair. And when he woke me the scene was blue-grey. The chair, the room, the bed, his suit, his hair – but Cary could look that way in film too, silver-blue, it was the way at the time, the style, the go, the rage. Anyway, when Cary woke me, the room was at an odd angle, opened out. It was like something from a play. We could have been onstage. I was half-asleep when I saw him sitting squarely in the chair. He did not flinch, or sit forward. He was very relaxed. He was so relaxed he had his legs slightly apart, the way men do. Don't get me wrong, he was fully dressed; he was dressed in his classy blue-grey suit, remember. And he was looking directly at me. Not menacingly. No, that was not his intention; but waking like that, seeing him like that, his look so fixed, it scared me a little, both mesmerised and scared me inside the belly and throat, deep inside where no one could see. I was sure he knew the effect he caused. Yes, he had a look of complete concentration more than intimidation, the not wavering, not even a blink, such a look, a stillness that made something in me fear that no amount of looking back could shift his gaze, or his lids, or my shame at being looked at so intently.

He was looking at me and not in any way caught out or shy at my waking, he was merely staring at me directly from the comfy big old armchair that he'd moved opposite the bed, as if he'd measured out the space between us while I slept. I imagined him doing that, the way my grandparents had for years sat opposite one another in their red chairs, one on each side of the hearth, for all their married life. Forty-odd years, smoking over each other, staring, laughing, fighting, loving – oh, the mugs of tea supped over the divide, so that when she died he carried on gazing at the empty chair he still called Ma ... The sound of her name becoming a bleat he'd so often made ... continued to make into the chair-back and wings ... Ma ... rion. When she died he quickly followed, both their indents pressed into the oilcloth, so that when I moved their chairs to help Father load them onto the bonfire, I found myself on my knees pressing my fingers into those dips in the floor, the patterns they'd formed between the four feet of one chair to the four feet of the other, plus their total of four legs, his open, hers crossed, measuring the distance that had held them together and apart.

Cary-as-Death surely had done this while I'd slept, shifting the furniture so that he achieved the maximum alignment; he was Death, for God's sake – his maths was impeccable – as impeccable as his suit and his hair and his ability to take on characters, people he knew I'd like; some foreknowledge that I'd had a thing for Cary Grant, always – *Houseboat* began it. Cary and Sophia. *Do it with a Bing Bang Bong*. Along with the story that En would repeat from time to time, about the morning he'd stopped off at a small corner shop in Bristol to pick something up, newspapers, pint of milk, who knows now, and in walked Cary. Yes, there he was, so tanned, so tall, so elegant and all the women swooning in the store, Cary from Hollywood, no less. Cary asking for cigarettes, explaining that he was visiting his dear old mother. Imagine the smiles, the after-talk, being that close, as close as I now was to Cary – Cary-as-Death, that is… I suspected that much, his nails were impeccable, filed, buffed, holding the arms of the chair so gently, so gently holding the antimacassars, as if he were holding me, his nails so perfectly finished. Even in death, post-death, as Death, he had the poise of a film star about him, the care of the studio, the attention of the undertaker to his hair, a pressed line to his trousers. And it was then that the phone rang – it was next to the bed. Cary's warm eyes, kindness now, but could I trust this? I answered the phone. It took some rings, but I answered. Heard his voice in my ear, distinctive, mischievous, the sound he made – who could mistake that voice, Cary's lips moving silently before me in time with the phone, working like a ventriloquist, telling me that he would only ever talk to me this way, via the telephone. That he was showing me things I was not ready to understand. Small pictures in his eyes as I moved closer, his eyes moving like one of those kaleidoscopes I'd gaze into for hours as a child, his eyes, what details, scenes, people and places I'd forgotten, forgetting fear, almost on my knees before him, almost about to reach out to steady myself on his hands – when he vanished. Vanished, leaving only gloves on the empty arms of the chair, one each side, gloves where his hands had been: a pair of blue-grey suede gloves, the lining blue velvet – no, neither the film nor the song. I wanted to push my hands inside – desired nothing more, feared nothing more, to push my hands deep inside the gloves.

And so it continued for nights after this, the gloves he'd leave, a deeper shade of blue, a slightly better fit each time… His voice on the telephone understood, recognised; his voice, his gloves, his hands.

Mert's story

This is not the story of a threat letter, rather a story of a violent threat that leads to a letter – a love letter of sorts – unexpected. To repeat: *Love is a kind of blackmail, always a demand,* Barthes said.

~

He was brought in at night to the ward … I'd worked the early shift that week. The ward was hot, the oversized key they'd given me warm in my hand, the oversized key opening up the ward. Locked wards, they called them; some were open and locked for different periods of time, depending on whether any of the patients had been detained or not under the Mental Health Act, sections of time, patients in and out, patience being the right word, the main requirement when you enter such a place. Patience, there will be periods of time when you will lose everything you took for granted, where nothing will happen, only the noise of nothing happening; doors opening and closing, the rattle of tea-trolleys, supper-trolleys, medicine-trolleys, waiting to know what your future will be.

He was seventeen years old, that's all; three years younger than I was at the time. Maybe he is not even alive any more, this person I am telling you about. He was sitting alone in the ward; it was 7am. No – I was always punctual for work; five to seven, then. Morning sounds echo, a sun not properly up, people walk rubbing their eyes, shifts changing, steady steps of departure and arrival, the hiss of gas, the first tea, bare feet on the linoleum, strong night's piss flowing in the pans, the sound of stockings against the starch of uniforms – only most are not up yet, just those doers already organising the trolleys with tea cups.

We handed over; the night nurses left. He was said to be dangerous, the seventeen-year-old admitted during the night. Violent. They used that word. People said they were worried about approaching him.

I do not recall who spoke first. He hadn't slept. He was sitting in the day-room on one of those red vinyl upright high-backed chairs, the curtains barely drawn behind, the gaudy floral chrysanthemums falling off their runners, the birds already drunk on reveille. I walked toward him, walked the length of the room because he didn't look violent to me. Does violence always have a look? I walked the length of the industrial carpet the way you might approach a wild cat with something held in your breath, in your smile, tone, eyes and hands. He looked scared. I wondered if I was wrong to be walking the length of the carpet in the half-light of morning, alone in the oversized room. I talked and kept a sensible distance, him sitting, me standing, the poise of escape. There were no other staff around; most were crowded into the small office still smoking the first cigarette of the day; gossip, laughter, slurping brown sweet tea. Someone in the distance said, Be careful of him! But I did not lose his eye, or turn; I took no heed, proceeded toward him, small steps, asking if he was OK. He didn't pounce. He asked if he was locked in. I told him he was. It's not normally like this, I said. It's because they say you broke your grandmother's arm. He did not blink or lose my eye. I began to believe he was much more afraid than me, so offered him a drink, food. To begin with he refused everything except the challenge of the gaze.

All I remember after this was a month of night-duty, a change of shifts, his insomnia turning into nights of chess. He showed me his best moves, his hand on my Queen, as I discovered sight in my new glasses; the unfolding of his story backwards each night over chess. How his father had moved away. Sent postcards. Cards the boy had pinned to his wall, alternating

65

pictures and messages. Mapping Father while his mother moved him and his sister into her bed. Taught them over time how to fondle her and each other. His mother drunk, regularly high or passed out. They sat one day for hours, he and his sister, watching over her body, thinking her asleep. They'd teased, joked, half-scared over her gin-soaked body filled with pills and death, her death on the stairs while they talked and laughed and planned their escape. Studied the map, the gape of her blouse and legs and mouth, places they'd entered, existed in her, in one another, returning to her in ways they had never expected when they realised she was gone, when they realised they had to call someone, those others who in turn separated him, that evening, from the sister he loved: he sent to an ailing grandmother – West; his sister sent East. No one knew what had taken place at home. No one knew why one evening while Granny shouted over him, he took her arm and twisted until he heard the crack, the crack as unexpected as his mother's breasts had been in his teenage mouth. He looked up the words they attached to him: psychopathic tendencies, personality disorder – he forgot the rest... The short bearded Scottish doctor with his pen and drugs and plenty of confinement papers, filled the empty boxes kept ready for labels...

When he left, months later, after I'd moved on to another ward, he left a large manila envelope for me. Saliva-sealed. Inside, ten packets of my then-favourite cigarettes, the red and gold spilled with a letter written on the back of a prescription ending *I love you* three times a day with food. It never fails to startle you. A letter and words you hadn't seen coming, words underlined in ink; held, hidden in case it was misunderstood, in case people thought I'd done something wrong. I love you between us, received, understood.

Every letter is a love letter, Kraus says.

I smoked the cigarettes, shared them. Kept the small letter.

Lost the letter. Maybe someone else found it. *I love you* mislaid, anonymous, a neat enough hand. *I love you* over a prescription for thirty major tranquillizers never taken.

Sue's story

For a long time my sister sent me very angry hurtful letters and nasty text messages. Before that were the abusive phone calls to our home, day and night, a lot of homophobic abuse. Until one day I told her that although she was my sister, she wasn't welcome, and I did not under any circumstances want her in our house. That was about eight or nine years ago. She lives hundreds of miles away in London and I remember coming home one night having been to the cinema and there was a message on our voicemail saying that she was in the village pub waiting for me. For ages I couldn't leave the door unlocked even when I was in the house, in case she turned up, walked in, and I couldn't get her to leave. Because she'd been, and still is I think, quite ill, I held back the absolute rage I felt in response.

I once burnt a letter my sister sent me. The first such letter I received from her, actually; it had shocked me so much that I burnt it.

Recently, though, I've wanted to write her a long letter about our childhood – if I speak to her she doesn't ever pause long enough to listen – but I don't know if I'd ever send it. The writing day we did recently coincided with these thoughts, and even to mention a sister in my writing felt strange, but the photo I conjured contained it.

Violence comes in so many forms. My mother told me that once, when she went to get a copy of her birth certificate in Jordan, the page had been ripped out of the records. There were various family arguments at the time, and my mum had received threats, so she thought it was quite deliberate. But to remove a birth certificate to me seemed such a violent act – someone wished she'd never been born. After she died my brother eventually went to live with my dad and his new wife and she told new friends that my brother was her son. It was totally believable as there wasn't much of a gap in age between him and my half-brother and they look so alike. And so my mother was rarely spoken about. Erased from his history, from our shared history.

I could go on...

Rosa's story

Just to say that my return here was brought about by being *driven out* of an area because of continued harassment by neighbours and the threatening, intimidating letters and the atmosphere of the whole area in which my children and I lived.

The anger I felt and the fear were consuming, but we weren't destroyed, and furthermore my children became so anti-violence, and so powerful in standing up for their beliefs and for friends or any person being threatened, that I realised we were all transformed by the experience in a positive and permanent way.

I remember at the time someone giving me a print-out saying *the best revenge is living well*.

Day Pages – Spain

In the gold room there are two paintings, copies, maybe some local's imitation, until I notice beneath the plantain and over-bloomed orchids – an unimaginative cliché for a so-called lost island – the name Gauguin, scrawled, the way a child might show off. In the large painting there's a woman with her back to us, her face almost in profile, turned toward a man to her right. On a thin pole she carries chillies and breadfruit. The man's dog has its tongue hanging out at the dog between the woman's thighs, more the suggestion of a dog, the painter's doggy hallucination arse-end out being gestured to by the other in the same way the man begins his command of the woman, Come here ... I want you. The sun is low on her calves, with no more strength than the woman and her dog trying to ward off the other's wants. It's the energy that's lost then for a moment, for the dogs, for her; for myself trying to think of things to tell you, to keep you interested, to keep things between us in motion ...

There's a knife in the small Gauguin painting, on the table in front of the central figure of a girl almost on the edge of puberty. A boy sits either side of her; they look into her face as if she will answer their question, as if she knows what to do next, how to move the scene along. Maybe she will take the knife pointed in her direction, hold the knife to the light that floods the room, plunge it into the sun or into the red fruit or herself or the boys one by one. Everything is upon her, especially the knife. Everything waiting to begin, will never begin.

That's not all ...

In the gold room where I write to you, there's also a copy of the painting *Las Meninas* made into a jigsaw. One piece of the jigsaw holds the eye of the little Infanta Margarita. The more I look the more I want to undo, can see this could occupy me for days, that I would have the patience for Velázquez' eyes underlined like a mask, for the shadowy figure in the doorway, the dog at the very front right of the painting. The dog walks from one painting to the next, this one less of a ghost. Most of the paintings we looked at in the Museo del Prado had a pooch somewhere in the foreground. Some of the dogs and their subjects wear matching bows. Faithful, gentle, mutts, for now not quite asleep but confident enough to rest while figures kneel, crouch, attend; ready to defend whatever royals and nobles, dwarves and little maids.

What could I jigsaw. The letter as jigsaw, imagine receiving it that way, in pieces, boxed. An image on the front, complete, blown up, letter as landscape. Looking for the edges, no sky to help you – Dear Mr … I await with interest … Mistaken kisses XXXX. Hurt in pieces; a jig I-saw-you-cut-up. It could begin a whole new slant to the post: letters you have to assemble. I find an article about a man called Ted, who spent fifteen years piecing together two thousand fragments of love letters to his late wife which she tore up when she caught someone reading them. His wife tore each one smaller than a thumbnail. Ted started his task of assemblage by separating each corner and centrepieces of the torn letters, putting them back together an hour every day over fifteen years. *When I first met my wife-to-be,* Ted said, *it was love at first sight.*

I've strayed like all good dogs.

In *Las Meninas* the dwarves make the Infanta feel she is taller than any child. The construction of the dog is visible in the light. Often we forget the dog. I want to touch the jigsaw but it is framed in glass that says I know your hands, your desire to trace a mouth, nose, chin. Can a letter have a face, can a letter breathe, have holes for air and waste, holes we can enter, trapped in time, trapped in a pose with the dog, in its histrionics and history.

The dog in the painting is faithful and forgets it can move, forgets it can make a run for it, forgets it's more than paint. You should see the guards in the Prado where the real painting hangs. Guards as still as the dog; if you move too close – I knew it – watch those guard dogs come to life.

In the gold room where I write to you, there are the three paintings and three mirrors. One dark oversized wardrobe. The sort you could live in if you had a mind to hide one day. That's how it was when I was small. We had our own wardrobes and each wardrobe had a mirror at the front between the two wardrobe doors. I believed that a man lived in mine. Monster man. The mirror held him and me in place at its centre, it made me part of the wood and glass, and part of his flesh: inside beneath the clothes, who lived? I dare not look, not then, not now. Not after dark. Now, I push my notebook under my clothes inside the wardrobe, in case the woman who brings fresh bed-sheets and towels each week can speak enough English to decipher these early scribbles; you inside the notebook, tucked inside our clothes, inside the wardrobe, the stranger behind the door. *Tall Boy*, she said, a woman I knew, a woman describing her room, she said *Tall Boy*, she said *Stand Alone*, and I loved the names and told her as much. We were writing about rooms and furniture and all the beds we'd ever slept in. We wrote ... *Walk ins, Goes unders, Go Between* – outside my field of vision, think and see laterally, a quick fleeting sense of something moving, something moves in the glass and catches my eye. Come live with me, En had said, third mirror to the right. We'll meet there each day, in the gold room. Keep going straight until you see the big mirror. Meet me there. Watch yourself deliberately walk the length of the room. Say – Leave matters here. Like someone on tiptoe, catch yourself on purpose, sometimes by accident, walking toward the mirror to check you exist. Who

73

ever can see what is passing away, who ever can see the point at which things change as fast as they'd began. A bed begins this book, a bed, a bedroom, an oversized wardrobe, a holiday beginning these pages to you, pages opening out from a gold room, a notebook, an oversized cupboard with mirrors, words scribbled each morning, shared each evening, to hide words and people and secrets and threats in sturdy reliable cupboards.

That sturdy rectangle, 6 by 4, pine, nothing fancy,

scrubbed, four twisted legs tinged pink, a little stained. We'd joke that the table knew everything. Friend Alan – who would sit with me each Friday afternoon at the kitchen table – would sometimes stop mid-story, rub his hands over the wood and say … Ah, if this table could talk, could tell all it has seen and heard, what conversations and joys and meals and occasions. The weddings where we tied red roses to the table edge, where a mother had placed a whole salmon on a silver plate with bunches of dill, braids of bread. The table where the children were placed and from where they almost kamakazied from their bouncy chairs when they were babies … remember. Remember the meals, the songs, the readings, all rehearsals, all soaked into wood, the tears, mad laughter, the announcements beneath the light of seven red plastic hearts.

At the table En always sits to my right, and visitors sit opposite. This is the order of things, the order of the table. Women prefer the wicker chairs at the ends: one end's mine. The men prefer the more solid upright chairs that are made of wood. The table's proven. In summer we cart the table outside for birthdays. Hang balloons from the grapevine over the table. Tie down the corners of the cloth with weights. The balloons pop as the sun heats them up, small explosions marking the day, the explosions we are never prepared for and so we jump each time.

Once you are around the kitchen table you know that things between us are changed. It's a threshold, like jumping over the broom, like being carried in his arms into the kitchen, carrying our babies home into the kitchen in our arms, the babies placed carefully on the table. M's story of Josette delivering her baby on a different wooden table, remember that. Everything scattered to the floor. The table the postman had bent her over – fucked

75

her – who could know the father of this child, a husband away at war, a postman delivering each day. Now a new kind of delivery and postman, years of knowing this story and I only just saw the coincidence in that. J, clutching the table top with the postman inside her, then delivering her child, legs apart, someone holding up a kerosene lamp, lamp and labour, red hair pushing forth from her wetness, the shape of a new son emerging onto the table. The table already scrubbed for breakfast, for Friday's fish later in the week. A fresh fish caught to mark a birth.

Friend Alan tells me that when he dies he wants to be buried in his Ka ... yes, his small silver Ka. Before that, it was a blue Fiesta, well rusted; we'd have to bump-start it each time he left to go home. In the end he was forced into a different model of final rest. Every Friday he'd sit at his end of the table; at my end I'd make tea. You have to know this about our home and our table: we have our given seats, our chosen ends. My doing, no doubt; I am, as they say, a creature of habit, habitat, routine, things in place, and our places at the table. His end, friend Alan, who'd come by each Friday, his place was under the dried red peppers threaded onto a string. Alan's end, nearest the door ... Ah if a table could talk, twenty-one years of life with us, the coming-of-age of a table. He sold his car, friend Alan, forgetting that it was meant to be his final mode of transport. The table was to be mine – or so he said – the table kept or handed down ... final coffin, we joked. This table turned upside down, where you could lay me inside, fill it with needed books and dress me warm.

We'd pull it out from the wall, the table, when we had guests, right side up, of course. Look at that, Claire would say, here we all are, here at home, in the kitchen. Here we are all gathered around the table; the occasion of the letter, defying the letter ... it's almost a painting, a supper – not last. Still, we break the bread, carry the bread to the table, spill the wine;

people carry flowers, tiny trees, food to the table, months of blooms. We photograph the wedding bouquet Claire brings. The pink English roses, the narcissi Rosanne sends me, the smell of chrysanthemums taking me back to the grave. How unfair that some flowers become locked into death, the lily in particular – maybe even the rose. For now, Paul is carrying bread to our table. Bread he made of wholewheat and tomatoes, white with black olives, the brown bread, and thin white baguettes. Paul makes the bread very early in the morning. He tells me this before he arrives, so we can anticipate the bread's arrival. We lay out the food and although the table is filled with small dishes of olives, pâtés, salad, hams, fish, aubergine, we leave a space for the bread, the breaking of bread, the passing and taking of bread.

From the opposite side of the table, Sarah says that Paul would have liked to be a baker, may still like to be. The pleasure of the early morning, something of this quietness goes into the bread, this hour and silence, clean hands; over the kitchen where he worked, others still asleep, dreams being made overhead, his dreams going into the bread as he mixes and kneads to prepare the bread for the visit; whole flour, rye, sour dough rising, yeast bubbling like an experiment. I am writing hungry. These words come back: to both knead and need the bread. The recipe he shares later when he drives the bread, miles to our home, bread wrapped in paper and cloth, bread he cuts at our table when he shares the recipe I can no longer remember, only strong flour, bread flour, telling him the story of the stones En collected once that looked like plump loaves, stones renamed bread stones, marriage stones. These words come back: bread knife serrated – I did not visualise that you would harm En with a bread knife. Knives were my biggest fear, but the bread knife was exempt. The bread cut thickly, the loaf placed cut-side-down onto the table – an old wife's tale to ward off harm, keep the luck face-down, safe and sound, held into the table. Fingers licked. Better torn, someone said, like in church when as a young woman I swear I only got baptised so I could join in on the breaking of bread. No wafers. Not then, a whole loaf passed around. Crumbled onto outfits. Flesh and fresh in our mouths, we cannot live without bread they say ... Bread now carried to the table. Cob, twists, plaits ...

You have made coming together an occasion – not so much a celebration, though maybe of friendship, of camaraderie, of safety in numbers. From the minute others hear about the letter, they call in, drop in, arrange to see us. We buy a lot of biscuits. A heart leaps when the doorbell rings, watch En go to answer it. The policeman passes the policewoman another chocolate finger and says – We have to learn to take fear out of the equation. A decision to stay in, STAY PUT, be safe. The table was always there, sixteen years back, it moved with us, the table that is always filled with flowers. These days, those days, post-letter, the scent of tiny daffodils delivered, fills the kitchen. Took away the smell the letter carried. The smell a threat makes.

Before the police leave, maybe their third brief visit, little progress, less than enough to nibble, they say they are doing their best; they say not to worry; they say it is common enough, in the type of work En does, for people to get letters like this; they say that one letter doesn't mean anything will be followed through. They ask if the alarms they fitted are working properly and to our satisfaction. We test and re-test. We pour more tea. They say they'll get someone to call around with personal alarms as well as the alarm they've installed that activates the station directly, the alarm that when pressed will call out the police without even the need of a phone call. They say they will secure the doors, get someone to fix a light out the back, arrange to analyse the fingerprints on the letter. Ask around, interview staff, eliminate prints – they say there is not much else that can be done.

After their visit, the drain man calls and I pass him a biscuit, not sure if he'll take it, considering his job and all, but he surprises me and asks for an extra Custard Cream, large mug of tea with three sugars. I tell him about the letter; I didn't mean too, it just came out. I was worried he'd seen the police leave the house and that he would think we'd done something wrong. I tell him about you. I had nothing to tell him as I know nothing of you, but I tell him of the letter. I don't show him, just explain. He makes sympathetic noises, he tells me he gets threatened all the time, more verbal than written; it's the Cleansing Department who get the written attacks, the office staff. He gets more of the face-to-face when people's houses flood and he meets them red-faced and knee-deep in shit.

He's kind and genuine, the drain man; in exchange, he tells me one of his dreams. It seems more than fair. A drain man so intimate with your waste can quickly become a friend of sorts. There we are sharing letters and dreams. It takes my mind off things as we talk and I watch him work. He dreams that his son's back is embroidered with bright turquoise stitches, beautiful designs, fish, all different kinds – would you believe it of a drain man? – Would you believe it, the drain man said of his dream, fish sewn into my boy's back in bright blue thread. He inserts the camera – he has it on a reel – it snakes into our drain and he convinces me that his job is worthwhile and that he enjoys it so. This encourages me to share my most recent dream, tit for tat.

– I dreamt of a car accident, I tell him, not a beautiful dream like yours. A woman was weeping in preparation for years of mourning … it's far too morbid, I say. – Go on anyway, he says, it's not your doing what the night brings. – In the dream I was making some food. No, in the dream it was not me but some kind of stand-in, lookalike, impostor. I insist on the third person, and considering the woman's loss everything seemed surprisingly composed and normal, I tell the drain man. Wondering about her grief I stared at her, knowing that she now knew something that I could not understand. Not that I wanted her loss, but I did want to understand something more of it, this stillness, this knowing that grief gave her. And I looked at her in the way a virgin looks upon a pregnant woman, the way a pregnant woman looks upon a nursing mother, the way a nursing mother looks upon a woman waving off her teenage son; in the dream all these women turned in the same direction to notice the grandmother watching her grandson carry a bucket of sand, watch him make a castle, reminding them all of how a child's eyes can turn green in the sun.

Just weeks after you first wrote, I receive a book in the post

sent from 35 Love Lane, New Jersey. I would like to move there; that's what I think as I open up the parcel, the book of dreams I'd ordered. *Dream I Tell You,* that was the title, HC's words again. I would like to move us all to 35 Love Lane, to go find it, to write this book to you from Love Lane.

Just weeks after your letter arrives, I am sent a postcard. People send us cards all the time in response to your letter's arrival: good wishes, thoughts and small words of advice. This card, it turns out, is not from anyone we know. It is from a company that is trying to sell a magazine, a magazine on censorship. They have no idea what they are doing when they send this image into our home – how could they? I have always read too much into signs and coincidences – this is not an apology, simply a fact. I received two packages that day, just weeks after you'd written, now that the post causes only suspicion, a degree of trepidation, just in case one letter becomes two, three, our daily bread. The post never fails to surprise you: when you are expecting things they rarely come; when least expected, things arrive and slap you awake. A postcard when I was still dreaming of Love Lane ... a postcard on censorship – or so it says, with an image of a mouth, a woman's mouth, a generous lipsticked mouth sewn together with stitches. The stitches were strong, the type En would use to sew the leather bags he'd sometimes make for me. The type of stitches people use to sew sacks and boots: strong, neat stitches on the diagonal. The lips were matt red, not gloss, but prepared, sealed with a kiss, too corny, with loving care, the stitches, you might say, were accurate; the holes had healed over, there were no visible or oozing scabs. I wondered how you would find and feed such a mouth. Depends on how long she'd been sewn up like that. Perhaps you could give drinks through a small tube, the type you might use to suck fluid out of a baby's lung. Let's say they feed the mouth cold water to quench her thirst to encourage her not to talk, or grunt, or mutter. This is the story I imagine. They feed her fresh water, the odd sweet juice, so that they can photograph her mouth close up, again, again, again. They push the camera close so that nothing else is visible, only the mouth and the stitches. They tell the woman that they will of course snip her mouth open again once the image is complete, but of course they forget, and she has to cut her own mouth open, after the photograph, late into the night – in the yellow light of the bathroom she takes her tweezers and nail scissors and when the stitches are pulled clean she moves her lips apart cautiously, watching herself gape into the mirror, form a sound she has never heard before.

Weeks after your letter we went to The Quad

with En to pick up various boxes of papers, files, things he
needed so that he could work from home where it was safe – or
so they said. While we waited for him, all of us together in his
office, the fact of simply being inside the building caused mad
laughter to break out of us – well, all of us except En.

D and I giggle uncontrollably – mainly because of the threat
of being there, the twists and turns and dark endless corridors
of the place, the concern on people's faces. Mainly because
once inside En's office, Hugo slips a tie over his head – a
tie that is left hanging, meetingless, Hugo playing at being a
Quad man. He gives a mock presentation and slicks back his
long hair, sticks some glasses on the end of his nose, asks me
to sort out his knot and to make it look as big as possible. I
make several bad attempts with a Windsor. Hugo says that The
Quad reminds him of a *Thunderbirds* set and that he is waiting
for the *5, 4, 3,* for the crew to prepare in the underground
car park, emerge from the open roof on level five, the direc-
tor's suite. As we leave we sing the *Thunderbirds* theme tune,
laughing: *the laugh that laughs at the laugh*, as M would say.
We hear the insincerity of it. Feel the protection of it. Laugh
so much the boxes in our hands spill. En's teasing apology;
others' awkward smiles.

Weeks after your letter The Quad reps visit, gather around
the table, the bosses with long overcoats and black shoes that
need polish, the Union man, the HR woman, the Health and
Safety woman. We buy more biscuits and four different kinds
of tea. We buy a bigger coffee pot and keep the beans frozen for
freshness. The Quad reps hold weekly meetings in our house
from then on. They take minutes, draw up action plans and care
plans for our safety. They send messages that say things like:

I am appalled
at what you
indicate is happening
and have given
my authority
for the matter
to be addressed
as fully
and
as rapidly
as possible…
The sentiments that I expressed
in my previous message
to you
still stand
and we will ensure
that you feel
supported
throughout
this
process.

While practicing self-defence in the kitchen, Hugo asks me if I know what the amygdala is… Before I can say yes, as it happens I do … he explains that it's the part of the brain where we sense fear. He says that he got this from a programme he was watching on ghost-hunting.

D tells me that if someone grabs you, you should always fall onto an attacker with your full weight, always move into the direction he is pulling, fall onto him, surprise him. Give him your full weight when he least expects it. I try this. D lifts me off the floor into the air where I dangle.

Weeks after your letter I get an invitation by post to attend a two-day event, Hélène Cixous reading from her work, by coincidence titled, *Let Her Letter Go...* As if she knew. I run to the place and we sit in a dusty hall, late, out of breath. I write her a letter inspired by her letter. I write that I would like to have heard her read along the corridors we ran through to get to her, to have heard her read among the chemicals and the Bunsen burners of the science labs we raced by.

HC reads and I scribble down notes in the half-light. Her hands covered in ink, almost a stigmata; when she begins to read, taking up the letter, ink bleeds everywhere.

She reads...

Whoever you are, deprived of an address, one never knows to whom a letter belongs.

We have never been together, but in reality we have been together dozens of times.

They could have died before having told one another their story.

The gravity that makes us want to drink tea together will have become slight.

No house without a door, no house without a family. The inside stranger.

Think of all the letters people wait for that will never come, all the ones that went missing, or were never posted at all. All that could have been, all you'd lost or been saved from, all those people who write letters for a living, people paid to write letters for people who cannot write. Dictation. The film we saw about a woman who works in a train station, she writes letters for people each day for a fee they cannot afford. Sets up a little table and a stool each morning. The intimacy of the letters she writes – says she will post – collects, decides, with the help of her sister each evening, which letters will be sent, held back, which to bin, burn, or tear apart.

The day your letter arrived, there were swans on the river, one swan's head held to the riverbank. She looked at first as if she was eating; eating or tugging at the weeds. In the end I wasn't sure if she'd caught her beak on something she couldn't free herself from, if her vicious jerks were caused by ferocious impatient hunger, or the fear of being trapped.

My fearsome, HC would call her. My fearsome, and I applied this to the swan.

I will not write this book, H writes. Titles her chapter. The brutality of the denial makes me realise that if I were told I must not write this book then I would not know what to do about the violence of it being taken away from me so soon. To see H's words there like a command: *You will not write this book,* meaning: *you must.*

Along comes the letter and I take it from him.

What are you going to do now? the letter said. And now what are you going to do?

You…

En's account of The Quad

From the age of twenty-seven I have worked in large institutions of some kind. The Quad is an institution just like any other institution. There have been times when I have worked outside of the big buildings with their miles of corridors, the corporate headquarters with floors stacked on floors. Looking back, I always felt happier working in smaller, more out-of-the-way places, but I have to admit that there is something about the size of those huge structures, the expanses of land they sit on, the physical and human layers and levels: they have their own allure. I worked in a huge Victorian mental asylum in the early seventies. Everything there was governed by strict hierarchies; you had to quickly work out where you belonged. For example, the way that people would sit at different tables in the staff dining hall depending on their status in the organisation. The doctors were the aristocracy, then the senior managers, then the professionally trained people: nurses, therapists, psychologists – but all ranked according to seniority, with three separate groups for trainees depending on which year of training you were in. Where I worked, this was denoted by the number of stripes on the nurses' epaulets, or different coloured belts. It did not take me long to discover that the labouring classes in the institution – the gatekeepers, the porters, the cleaners, the secretaries – had a lot of power too. They knew all the secrets and the gossip about everyone else. They also knew all of the perks. Those were the relationships to cultivate if you wanted to get anything done; all was orderly, you knew your place.

I was fascinated by the geometry, the long corridors formed, north, south, east and west, and the ridiculous names they gave to the wards: after trees for instance, ash, oak, poplar, or the more obvious system, E14, denoting the 14th ward on the East corridor. There was something mysterious about certain sections of the place that you rarely visited, parts of the building where special teams of people worked, apparently doing something like 'rehabilitation', only to discover later that nothing at all happened in those places. And then there was the chapel and the synagogue. Yes, nearly half of the patients were Jewish in that North London asylum, many having swapped the death camps for the mental institution where their new captors were struggling to acknowledge that they might have different cultural needs: *We give the Jews sausages for breakfast because they can't eat bacon.* I quickly discovered that they were pork sausages, but most of the Jewish patients ate the bacon as well. Tea was served out of giant aluminium teapots with the milk and sugar already stirred in.

Many of the staff who worked in those places were as institutionalised as the patients: the nurse who used to come back to the ward where she worked on her day off to steal her daily loaf of bread and bottle of milk – even though the bus fare probably cost more than her free contraband; the male staff nurse who dressed from the patients' pool of clothing, daily sifting through the pile in the laundry room for a complementary tie and shirt. Even in the late seventies there was no individualised clothing for the patients. Others lived and worked in the hospital, rarely leaving the grounds. They would drink until late at night in the staff social club, occupying the same seat for years with the same work colleagues. There were dart, cricket and football teams; they even held annual beauty contests in the hospital in which rival contestants and their supporters would often come to blows. Some of the staff got married in the hospital church and held their reception in the social club. And inevitably, there was the ongoing round of scandal about who had left or was sleeping with whom. The institutional social club has become a thing of the past now, as most such places have an alcohol ban, and all now have a smoking ban. But shades of institutional life still flourish.

The Quad was a modern version of this kind of structure. A huge place, built on the four sides of a quadrangle, each side a mirror image of the other. Once inside the building, especially if you were new, you could easily forget whether you were on the north, south, east or the west of the building. There were few distinguishing features. They even had identical men and women's toilets in each of the four corners and on each of the five floors. Some people had this habit of going to the toilet on a different floor from their own – not to shit on their own doorsteps, as it were. In the middle of the ground floor of the building there was a huge open area, the actual quadrangle. You could take a shortcut by walking diagonally from the inside of one corner of the building to the opposite corner. They used to have a summerhouse in the centre of the quadrangle where people used to go to smoke, a reverse of Foucault's Panopticon in *Discipline and Punish,* because in the case of the summer house it was the smoker under surveillance from the four sides and five floors of The Quad: *Geometry as threat.* No one is allowed to smoke at work any more, so they took away the summerhouse. In addition to the five storeys there was a basement and an underground car park, but only the really privileged people were given spaces there. On each floor of The Quad there were offices on both sides of the corridor. The ones on the inside looked over the quadrangle, but I was lucky enough to have an office on the other side that looked onto the outside world. The fifth floor contained the penthouse offices where only the most important people worked.

The separate little teams in each part of The Quad were cliquey and competitive. Then you had all the different *corporate* departments that everyone had to deal with: Human Resources, Finance, Payroll, the Legal Section, Audit, Accounts, IT, and of course the Unions. Then, most important of all, were the receptionists. In a way it was like an extension of school, so many damn rules about what you could and couldn't do and the ways you had to do things. There were the same little rituals that you get everywhere: the tea fund, the lottery, the leaving dos, and a month before Christmas all the secretaries decorated the offices and organised bran tubs. The Quad had its own post room where the letter would have arrived and would have been opened; outgoing mail would also get sent there, franked and sorted and despatched. The mail always came to us opened and stamped to say it was received on a certain date. In the case of the letter it was stamped 5th of March.

People at The Quad had no uniforms, apart from porters and kitchen staff, but the way people dressed was of course very uniform. I tended to dress down. The women could more or less wear what they wanted, but although there was no dress code, the men always wore jackets, white shirts and ties, all the trappings of ordered institutional life: fire drills, health and safety people – this big machine that generates itself. The reason you are actually there obviously drives it along, but the things that dominate are all the internal activities, habits and repetitions just like family life, people having rows, people who can't stand one another, people having affairs, people in competition, bosses that bully staff and staff who bully other staff, people who never do anything or are always on the sick, people who are obsessive workers and are there all hours of the day or night. And there are always the dramas: someone has got sacked for doing this or that, someone dies suddenly.

The letter was one of those dramas, but when you are on the receiving end you can't enjoy the gossip of it, you can't have that voyeuristic pleasure of seeing something happen to someone else. When something like that happens to someone else you always have a certain sort of smugness, that although it is happening to them, it for sure isn't happening to you. And so when something like that happens, the person on the end of the gossip is getting all the attention but being the centre of that kind of attention is not what you want. You just want to be one of the anonymous again.

En's risk assessment from the Quad

HAZARD
Look only for hazards
which could result in significant harm
Use the following examples as a guide

- Slipping   /   tripping hazards
        •
        Noise
    • Electricity
      • Fume
      • Fire
    • Vehicles
      • Dust
        •
      Violence

      Chemicals
        •
    Moving parts

    machinery
        •
      Manual
      Handling
  Work at height
        •
      Ejection
    of   materials
        •
  Poor   lighting
        •

92

Pressure   systems

•

Low   temperature

People

WHO MIGHT BE HARMED

- Disabled persons
- Young persons
- Inexperienced staff
- Visitors

•

Lone Workers

•

Pregnant/Nursing
Women
Mothers

Husbands
Fathers
Lovers

**IS THE RISK ADEQUATELY CONTROLLED?
WHAT FURTHER ACTION IS NECESSARY TO
CONTROL THE RISK?**

If possible
in the following order:

•

Remove the risk completely

•

Try a less risky option

•

Prevent access to the hazard
(eg by guarding)

•

Organise work to reduce exposure to the hazard

Issue   personal   protective   equipment

Employee and family – to be or not to be
Community alarm to be fitted
Markers on telephone line,
house
and car
arranged with police
Checks carried out
under car
Car parked away from outside house
Alternative vehicle offered
Remove existing details off internal directory.
Alternative accommodation offered
hotels – cottages by the sea – secure unnamed locations
Mechanism to be fitted to the letterbox to prevent anything
being
pushed through
into
the
home.
Community Safety
to arrange safety assessment.
Quad will pay for additional precautions
Eg.
Spy hole on front door
Etc.

Etc.
CCTV offered
declined at this stage but will review
Personal alarm issued
Personal alarms
Also offered to
wife
and
children
declined at this stage but will review

Return to Work
All visitors to the building report to Quad reception,
signed in and escorted
while in the building
with member of staff
to appropriate meeting place.
All staff members
are issued with
ID cards
and can only
enter building
using ID card
Quad reception staff
have been reminded
of actions
they should take
if enquiries/requests
to see
the employee
are made.
Staff reminded
not to provide

confidential staff details
to anyone
seeking them -
Transport offered
to and from home
with same taxi driver
Pass for underground car park to be issued
Secure meeting rooms are available
named employee
to be
accompanied
at meetings
and not to meet anyone
on a one to one basis.
Where appropriate meetings
to be held
in secure locations
Staff in post room
to be briefed
to ensure
any
handwritten
letters
/
packages
addressed to
the named employee
should only
be opened
by a
nominated person -
opened
carefully

to ensure
minimum contact
with enclosures.
If contents
are
of
a threatening nature
the envelope
/
package
and the
contents
should be
carefully
placed into
a plastic folder,
put aside
and a
nominated officer
notified
immediately
to deal
with the situation.

•

Think before you print

Let me get to the point . . .

I never think of you as a woman. I mean, when all's said and done, we all assumed you were male. We always dressed and addressed you as *He*. And imagine if I am wrong, naive again. Imagine if I am speaking with you, to you, to the wrong gender, in the wrong tongue and undergarments. How, I wonder, would that change my tone. If I saw you without facial hair, if I saw you in heels, if I began to imagine your breasts, your scent; would this change the sound of my voice, could it, should it? For sure there's hesitation if I imagine you in a dress, if I call you Denise, or Beth – personally, I've always liked names beginning with M: Matilde, Martha, Maud, Myrtle less so, but it stuck – if I imagine you picking up your kids while you pop the letter in the post, if I see you applying the same shade lipstick as me, shaving your legs in the same direction, rarely bothering in winter, under woollen tights, dark black stockings; if I imagine the letter in your handbag, next to the two-ply-tissues, the 3-for-2 offers at Boots, the small roll-on antiperspirant, the tooth floss, the tiny drawing your son made for you crumpled now, a forgotten drawn rabbit, the Band-Aids, the list for supper, too many old shopping receipts, the telephone number of your gynaecologist, your purse bulging with too many two-pence coins you always forget to spend, the driving license photo in which you had short hair because you were just beginning your career, no endorsements, pens, the one the kids bought you for Christmas, filled with water and snow, a winter scene over the Alps, the pen never works but still, you keep it anyway...

If...

I can never presume you are alone, yet I always think of you as singular, a single white male pronoun. Maybe something in the language ... something in the words ... the tone ... the pace ... the terminology...Yet wasn't it you who changed the pronoun from I to we – *we*. I hear you are short, you wrote to En, short men are the most bitter, this will give me and my collegues more pleasure when we finally meet up with you... The *me and my* changing the pronoun from I to we, here the *I* began its multiplication, when all along it was a letter to En: singular; to my husband: official. His name at the top left-hand corner, Dear Mr... Yes, you could ask who formed his I into *we*...This me, we.

All petty nonsense you could say, all splitting hairs, but you could also say that your use of the word *family* brought me into it. A letter to him alone that said, Your family will be OK but be sure you will be hurt... You could say that this sentence not only brought me into it, but brought our two boys into it – three, counting the one who lives away. You could say that with that sentence, *la familia*, you brought not only the three boys and me into it but whatever extended familiars that word encompasses. You could say that with the word *family* you called upon us all. Called in on my uncles, aunts, grandparents, the whole bus full, the whole Christmas get-together, weddings, funerals, occasions, all the clan gathered into motion. Mothers on either side, no sisters my side, two on En's, more than enough cousins, stepchildren, the newborn babes, the newly-weds, the in-laws, the pregnant niece. Yes, all knew about the letter. We talked of nothing else, friends too, all rounded up in your sentence, *family*... All of us worried, got involved, rolled up our sleeves, kept vigil – this is how families work, most often, most likely. Some write letters themselves, of harm, of retribution, of disillusion, misdemeanours, petty fights – families can be tricky too, we all have them, but in this case we all became part of it, the same concern. This is what happens ... it would be naive to think otherwise. Your family will be OK but be sure you will be hurt... This sentence going nowhere, trips up on itself, as I ask you, how can you love a man, even a cat or a rabbit come to that – the attachments we make along the way – yes, how can you love someone you've shared your life with, your everyday with, your day-to-day, your sleep and your shit with – let's not be coy here, we've gone beyond that, metaphorically and literally, we've moved on from that – I will not reach for the metaphors here, I will try to keep it plain between us, I will try to put my side, your side, my side, as plainly as I can, without simile, a table laid out simply to take the overabundant fare, to set off the gluttonous roasted goose and parsnip's nose of over-gravied work politics – yes, when the person you love is being threatened, that same person you have shared your afterbirth with, your hangovers with, your dreams, your moods, your fears, your innermost most incoherent thoughts with, the whole cotton box, all of it, so much, over twenty or more years, no, you cannot share all of that and then say, your family will be OK but be sure you will be hurt… It is a sentence that goes nowhere, that completes itself and becomes redundant. It's a sentence that cancels itself out as it goes along, that commits suicide as it unfolds family; hurt; be OK: an impossible string, an impossible position; completely without fail without doubt an impossible arrangement of words.

Paul's story

At home when I was young, well over forty years ago, we'd have an annual event prior to each bonfire night. Gangs of kids would all try to build the biggest most impressive constructions; all try to get the award for the best bonfire accolade. Because of this the bonfire building on the common became very competitive. One year our gang of boys was busy building our bonfire on the common, but we were worried that we couldn't find all the materials to make it large enough, that ours wouldn't be tall enough to be the best. The bonfires got so big we'd make small dens inside where you could sit and hide. Concerned that ours wasn't growing quickly enough, we decided to raid the house of an old lady who lived near by. She was eccentric and had a big rambling house. While she was out we broke in and took her antique harmonium, plus her piano. We rifled through her things and found bundles of old letters and photographs. We decided to take the lot. We didn't read the letters – I don't really remember if we did – but we knew they were letters and that she'd kept them together bound with string. Anyway, we took the lot and wheeled the piano and harmonium out and we broke up the instruments. Later, threw them on to the bonfire along with her letters and photographs. When the bonfire night came we burnt it all. No one ever caught us. We heard no more of it.

Ollie's story

Something popped into my head after I spoke to you that I haven't thought about for years. I think it was your talking about *The Letter* and your interest in letters and communication between people.

I was sixteen, living in Riyadh in Saudi Arabia, and the phone rang at 2am. It didn't stop ringing so I answered it; it was an English-speaking woman on her honeymoon in Amsterdam. She sounded desperate. Her new husband was not with her and she was not sure where he had gone or if he would return. He had written her a letter and left it for her on their hotel bed. The letter said that he'd changed his mind, that he wanted out and was leaving, threatening that if she came looking for him, he would get someone to hurt her. She was alone in their room randomly dialling numbers to find someone to talk to her. She had no idea where in the world she had dialled. She spoke to me for about half an hour, crying most of the time. She may have woken up the next morning and had toast and Marmite and strong black coffee or I might have been the last person she ever spoke to. Anyway, it has no bearing on anything, but as you brought it into my mind I thought I would tell you. Unless of course you *are* the woman, but I hope you aren't!

Caroline's story

At the end of my MFA in the States, I worked collaboratively with a friend and also with another guy who later became my husband, now my ex-husband. The piece we did together for our final show was a project based on graffiti, toilet-art graffiti. We used much of the graffiti we found and presented it in photographs and video pieces.

After the work was complete and shown, my then-to-be husband and I went for a needed break to the coast. We were camping in a small tent on the beach. Nearby were camp facilities you could use: showers and toilets.

In the mornings we'd wake and open up the zip of our tent and find pornographic images scattered around our tent, pictures that had been torn out of magazines, very explicit.

One night I woke. My husband-to-be was asleep beside me. I saw a torchlight pressed into the tent. It was so close you could see the filament. I woke K and said there was someone outside. He was so half-asleep that he didn't believe me, persuading me that I was imagining it and that I should go back to sleep.

In the morning we woke again to the same porn scattered around our tent. K walked over to the shower block. Came rushing back soon after saying that we had to leave – to get out of this place now. In the toilet someone had written our names, identified us and said they had been watching us have sex inside our tent and had been enjoying what they saw. It was written in graffiti on the toilet wall. We packed up and left straight away.

Martha's Story

The girl in question is nineteen and has stalked a friend of mine for a couple of years through various online forums and blogs. They've never met in real life, but they came to know each other on a forum celebrating works of fiction. They never argued, but the stalker became obsessed with my friend.

A few weeks ago she turned her attention to me. She has never contacted me directly, but has splashed my name around various blogs, including several run by my friends.

I was very shocked when I saw the postings. I only knew of it because she suddenly came onto my literary blog (a reviewing collective – there are 15 of us) and started attacking me. I had no idea what she was talking about, and didn't reply to her. On her blog I found a vitriolic rant about me. It was then I realised that she was the same person who had stalked my friend.

My cheeks were stinging and my heart racing when I read that first post. Oddly, I felt sorry for her, and my first reaction was to want to apologise for whatever I had inadvertently done to upset her. I later became aware that she was popping up on other blogs, posting nasty messages about me, and seemed to spend quite a lot of time hoping I would die…

She recently went quiet for a few days and I hoped I'd heard the end of it, but then she appeared last night and posted on my friend's personal blog. I actually started shaking when I read it – the laptop was literally bouncing on my knees. I found it difficult to sleep last night. My husband is very supportive, thankfully, but he's understandably quite bewildered and angry with all this.

I've talked it through this morning, and feel less disturbed; her written attacks are so irrational that half of me wants to laugh. I'm not afraid of her exactly, it's more that I feel exhausted at the prospect of having to deal with her indefinitely.

I would rather disconnect my internet connection than put up with years of this – but I know that's what she wants, so I am trying to act normally and keep up with my obligations.

I appreciate you keeping it anonymous.

Day Pages – Spain

This morning we heard a sound like a dragon straight from a fairy story, a dragon in the high blue sky. When Hugo had rushed from his bed, dragged me from my room to – Come look! The people who had been in the sky, inside the balloon's basket, now emptied out from the same enormous wicker container that had been carted here to the square on a truck. The balloon now folded, its dusty colour still visible. Four people climbed out, then another three. There were many hugs and much laughter. I worried that they might have seen us from the sky, watching and pointing up at them while we tried to wrap the curtains around our half-naked bodies, but no one gave any indication that they recognised us, dressed or otherwise.

We sit, En and me, just yards from the house we've rented, while the children lie around taking their time to properly wake. We sip coffee, read, talk across the table. I watch people smoke, men pouring themselves amber cognac, early morning sounds of bustle, small mopeds humming, dogs sniffing the legs of people and chairs, women carrying large straw baskets, buying bread from the local bar where they bake it out back. The pleasure of buying the bread, carrying bread, each time the same gesture, warm bread slipped under a cloth, breaking apart the crust. The heat escaping, sopped into green oil. Mopping up the juices, spreading the tomato and oil or *mantequilla*. Reminding me of the bread Dali painted, the bread in a basket that he turned into a hunk of gold. At Gala's house, another time, another year, the way we'd stood together and I'd wondered if En were to build a house for me, as Dali had for Gala, what elephants there would be in the garden. If we'd had more time and money, what crowns would we fashion, what plates patterned with playing cards, silver cutlery, what chequered floors and tiny dresses and patios overlooking yellow fields. What mirrors overlooking candelabras, dried flowers reflected in what I'd forgotten of their names. To paint the one you love in corners. Hidden easel, all dust – years gone and on, seen through door cracks. Where we'd peered in. Tried to touch the blue bed where Dali slept after Gala's death. To powder his face blue in her dressing room, run a bath. The water flowing from gold taps twisted like tied ribbons. The fire stoked to keep him warm; still embers in such sun. More small beds, red, gold, blue; the three bears hidden somewhere in the grounds. To take our turns on the gold sofa, eat in the main hall while we sat on the throne also draped in kingfisher blue. Polish the tiles, find the cool water in the garden again, the small font and broken stone, the sound of a parrot never seen. Remarking how the white cat lingered to make the place her own – we all pretended that she belonged to Gala. Could a cat this young have been owned so far back? It became its own legend. The white cat beneath the orange and blue cars, a cat that hid when it grew tired of being filmed. Hid before we all slunk away to the crypt where it was cool and dark and we wondered what the benches were for. What audience there. The yellow blooms on Gala's side of the bed; their resting place king-size compared to the tiny beds they'd inhabited in life, all through the upstairs rooms, the beds, the sound of opera, as silent now as her empty dresses. His side of the crypt empty – the side he had insisted he was to be buried while others decided he should rest elsewhere, and laid him in a floor miles from here. To hear yourself say inside the dark echo of the crypt, I still have the feeling that I should like to take a hammer, pickaxe, spade, and go dig him up from the gallery floor, unearth him from the marble in Figueres and bring him back to Gala. To La Pera, to the dark crypt where over our heads the white horse pulled back an eye to inspect all who passed by, still waiting for the grip of his master's thighs.

When your letter arrives

En places a baseball bat inside the front door, a bat he bought years back on a trip to see relatives in New York. Yes, he retrieves it from the loft, a full-size baseball bat now kept in a basket with the umbrellas, the strewn shoes and newspapers. It makes us laugh, a high-pitched gaggle that people make in unison when they are nervous and laughing from absurd embarrassment, from being unsure of what they are doing. D says it is over the top, but no one removes it. Sometimes D and Hugo pick it up, swing it around, laugh, pretend they are attacking each other, and then place it back into its new home.

Two women come around and fix more alarms. First the police fix their alarm – the one that we decide to keep under the TV, hidden a little beside the videotapes. The machine is white and has a huge glowing red button that if pressed instantly informs the police. The button is both reassuring and worrying, a constant reminder of you. It comes with a pendant that does the same job, an ugly plastic accessory that can be worn around the house, or if En is working in the garden, or taking out the rubbish, straying from the unspoken parameters of the kitchen. The sort of alarms older people wear if they are housebound and might need help if they should fall. The pendant hangs on the wall beside the front door over a rather wonky plate made by one of the kids. We carry the pendant from there to bed each night. It becomes part of our bedtime ritual, the glass of water I always take up, feeding the cat, checking the locks, windows, coal the Aga, downstairs alarm, phone, pendant carried up and kept over a photograph I have of En taken when he was in his late twenties and working in Israel. In the photograph he is surrounded by a flock of sheep. That was his job, to take the sheep out very early before 5 am. The sheep and the pendant.

Days later, while getting myself ready for work, the children for school, two women arrive with power tools. I don't mean to sound sexist – whispering to En that I'd expected blokes! They seemed confident enough and something in their presence at first unnerves me, then reassures. The six-inch bolts they apply to the doors, the sound of their drills as I write my morning emails. The women do not in any way falter; they have our new post box fitted over the inside of the letterbox flap in under ten minutes, so that mail will no longer fall to the floor, no more old-fashioned post on the mat, only an oversized cream metal box that will immediately extinguish anything flammable, jets of water that could soak the mail to a sludge. We make the ladies tea. It is a little early for biscuits, but we offer them anyway.

D comes downstairs as they are applying a peephole and a safety chain alongside the black bolts. – It's all a bit over the top isn't it, he says. What if I mess it up and do something wrong, set everything off by mistake? The ladies, who speak as one, reassure D, showing us both how to release the pins from the personal alarms, like a shrill hand grenade, the pinned alarms we are to carry whenever we leave the house. One that looks like a large felt-tip pen, activated by a gas; pressing it will release a sound piercing enough to deafen anyone who comes too close, the ladies say. Telling us story after story of their work, the ladies give examples of many types of house crimes, threats, tips on locks and the latest types of security measures and misdemeanours. They seem so concerned for us that it only makes me worry more: maybe I am missing something and things are even worse than we imagine. They remind me of the *Two Fat Ladies* who used to cook together on TV and travelled around in their bike and sidecar. Not that the women are fat – it is more the way they speak at the same time, are obviously very close and caring with each other, possibly a couple, from what they say, the way they seem to have a home life together; the way they fit together and are confident in their work – at ease with the way they take it upon themselves to seal us in, to complete their separate tasks so swiftly and confidently, in the way Clarissa and Jennifer might prepare and serve up a slice of stuffed pig's trotters in less than fifteen minutes.

I don't remember at what point we were advised by The Quad to ring what they called a trauma counsellor.

As much as we felt held hostage by your words, afraid to go out, to stay in, and to walk in the garden or the front yard freely, the title *trauma counsellor* seemed extreme. If I am honest we felt foolish, had not imagined we were in need of any kind of counselling – trauma or otherwise.

We resist; counselling is not something – despite years of working in what you could say was the business – that we'd ever turned to. The word *trauma* was confined to atrocities I could not imagine, worst-case scenarios, acts of genocide, violence played out, the body torn, harmed, hacked, shot, buried, taken. But people insist. Tell us it will help us get us through and on. It is hard to know sometimes if The Quad people emphasise it only because they have to be seen to be doing all they can to fulfil the action plan they drew up for us. Maybe that's unfair. Either way, we insist that if we do talk to someone, it should be someone neutral, someone we choose, not someone connected to work, because work was the cause of the letter. Sceptical enough, tongue-in-cheek, well-versed in finding suitable arrays of professionals: handymen, decorators, hairdressers, drain men – yet all this is new to me. And there I am on the phone, talking to a woman I know a little; she is already explaining to me that if we decide to work with her – which we will not – she likes to work with visualisation...

Which reminds me of a friend saying that surely whatever fears were unleashed in us on receipt of the letter were in many ways all the fault of television, our over-egged imaginations growing from oversized flat screens, each evening more drama and four-part series. Recalling that when I worked in Probation, painting with the lads, all of us squashed into one small art room, their favourite programme was *Crime Watch*. No joke, like a chef watching *Delia*, like a nurse watching *Casualty,* or *ER,* the rag-and-bone man watching *Steptoe.* What programmes, I wonder, would you watch in the evenings. What *Crime and Misdemeanours*, what whodunnits, forensic science, bombings, *Porridge, Count Down* the words, another syllable, consonant and vowel please… Yes, we all agree since the letter arrived that you, me, all of us in our time must have watched a few too many films, too many dramas, news items and cop shows, too much gore, kicking, strangulations, knife wounds.

Visualise this.

There I am on the phone, a long wait, still – not the dream phone with Cary, not that, this is some time later. I only listen out. I only listen out for En, listen to the woman on the phone, listening and looking have become my job. The looking and listening out for En… That's the deal, to love and to cherish, the man, the undershirt, the belly. That's what happens, the looking and listening-out.

Still early days, still taking advice, still listening out, listening to her tell me that when something like this happens, when such a letter arrives, enters your home – all we take for granted about our comfort and safety within that home – we visualise all sorts of awful things, she says. By undoing the visualisations, facing and taking apart these images that go around in us, all we create from our fears, from the dark corners of our twisted imaginations, we can begin to deal with what's happened, to find a way to put back in place some of our routine, to begin the work of redressing and keeping our fears in check.

I say nothing, but want to confess that since the letter arrived I repeatedly visualise the knife, En's belly – the bed. It's like the film with Marlon Brando, I want to say, but feel far too foolish to … not yet…

WAIT –

Visualise this.

I am on the phone, my mouth and mind clacking open and closed, moving like one of those wooden dolls and no arm in my back, and there I am saying, not saying: Since the letter arrived, every night in the dark, I listen out for the tiniest of sounds. Listen out for En's breathing, inventing sounds, staring through the window each night, below into the darkness of the garden, into the swaying of the trees, the nest in the distance, the wings of the crow; mind eventually lying down, giving itself up and over, travelling, drifting. There I am each night keeping vigil, turning on my right side, covering my hands over the soft belly, keeping his belly safe, inside the sheets, under the goose-feather duvet, my hands curled around the soft unprotected spaces of another's body, heart, liver, spleen, guts. I cover it all, had it all covered, or so I thought. Until that scene kept replaying – you know that scene, the film with Marlon, where the guy wakes up and the horse's decapitated head is in the bed, blood all over, surely cold by now. Iconic. And no way of knowing any more what or whose blood is whose, horse, head, belly. That's the scene that keeps rewinding when I wake… I don't say, ask, know, how you got past me in my sleep, afraid to pull back the sheets.

Sometimes I worry that I called you up.

That I made this happen. A ridiculous notion, I know, but I get my superstitious side from Great-grandmother: do not bring blossom into the house, do not cut your fingernails on a Friday, eat your fish from head to tail, no cut hair down the toilet, no shoes on the table, no hat on the bed, a bee in the house means there's a visitor on their way, a bird in the house is a sign of death…

In the week of the letter two crows take to our tree. En researches the meaning. The corby, it says, singular – one on the roof means death. That stays with me, especially post-letter, again no pun. I look for birds, hoping to see them together, always; the caw, and their nest almost blown away in the gales to come. I used to believe that if I lost something precious – I am not thinking of people, but maybe it could extend to that too; I was thinking more of things like pets, objects, books, jewellery – if I sometimes lost or mislaid something precious, I used to think it was because I hadn't cared for it enough, had taken it too much for granted, had the wrong kind of dismissive thoughts, had cussed it by mistake, a slip of the mind, of the tongue, causing its disappearance. For example, many years back a boyfriend bought me a small gold bracelet for Christ-mas. At the centre of the bracelet was a small diamond. I didn't think that the size of the diamond was a sign of his meanness, or any lack of affection; rather, I saw the choice as a matter of delicacy, the delicacy of the diamond, nothing too gauche. As I put the bracelet on for the first time, or rather he did – my eyesight has never been the best, and bracelets are often impos-sible to attach with one hand, all that wrangle and slip – as I looked at him fixing it, as I held up my arm, admired it, made what I imagined were sincere enough whoops, how beautiful it was, how much I loved it and would treasure it … all the

114

time I was wondering whether I cared for him enough. How little he knew me, this man, after what must have been at least three years together by then. How little he knew of me, the me who would never choose such a diamond, or come to that *any* diamond; gold or entwined hearts.

Hours later we were at work – it was Christmas morning but we were together on a day-shift on the wards, thirty psychotic men, the tree, the tinsel, the carols, sherry with the bacon breakfast, crackers already being passed around and ripped open – mainly by the staff, all wearing an array of paper hats while people paced the corridors steadfast in their delusions, cradling the baby Jesus. And when I looked down at my wrist – or was it that someone asked me that same old laborious Christmas question, And what did you get for … maybe it was then that I held up my left arm. I remembered that much, which wrist he had secured in gold – but that same left wrist was now empty!

I am sure that the sight of my naked arm made me want to shed a few tears – more for him than for myself, but try as I might I couldn't summon them. I was ahead of him and felt only the guilt, the sorrow of deceit, that my bracelet was lost and so too were we. We searched all over for the bracelet, under and inside beds, breakfast trays, laundry, medicine cabinets; we turned out pockets – not my idea, I might add. People accused people. I accused myself. Secretly I knew it was me who had done this. Not literally or willingly, but in not wanting his gold and diamond enough, if at all. We ate a second breakfast while the searching went on, while the suggestions continued about where and when and how – but it never was found. I was left to describe the gift as elaborately and as lovingly as I could when, for the remainder of the day, people – those who had not yet caught up – asked me the same question passed down from Santa's grotto – And what did you get? Yes, for hours and days afterwards, reading too much into my innermost lies, I believed it was my uncaring, unworthy ways that were teaching me the lesson: that I alone had caused this to happen, had surely only brought this on myself…

~

For weeks after the letter's arrival I'd take a short walk to the museum, trying to keep working on my book, the one about my son. Trying to distract myself from your words by making more of my own. Before, I should add, En stopped going into work, post-letter – before it was felt that it wasn't safe to stay at The Quad, to be out and about on Quad business. He would ring me from meetings, as always, not to discuss the contents of his sandwich any more, but to say that he didn't know what to do, where to be, how to be; since the letter people were escorting him from place to place like bodyguards. At a meeting that took place in a building run by an order of nuns, he rang me from a chapel – of all places. He had wandered off, not knowing what to do, where to be, En ringing me at the feet of our lady, a Jewish cynic atheist in a Catholic church… I laughed. Agreeing he should come home, take some time off, to be safe, until he knew who had written to him, until the police could find out more, maybe even find out who you were; we will never find out who you were and are, not really, guesses aside, safe bets and odds-on favourites – we can never be sure. But he came home that day and stayed home for some weeks.

When he rang me that day I told him that I'd gone to the museum as always, to try to write, try to distract myself. To get away from the claustrophobia of the house, a home that no longer felt safe and sound, private and secure. I agreed to meet him at the house soon.

Soon, I say. I tell him that on the way to the museum I

116

found myself thinking about the XXs of the letter. Not literally kisses in this case, more your crossings out, or the appearances of error. I know kisses were not your intention but there I am as always making imaginative leaps. I'd been thinking of the letter's array of XXXs as kisses, when I remembered The Kiss – Rodin's, that is, at the museum. The Kiss, not something I was fond of – the sculpture, I mean: I have no objection to a kiss. Yet maybe that too is a lie and while I have no complaints about my personal experiences of kisses to date – although there have been a few that I regret, surely common to all, those first fumblings in the picture house, behind the school gate – it was witnessing others caught in that locking of mouths that would sometimes make me want to turn away. Something too needy in it, too private, too slavering and human; potentially endless when the mouths of others are secured for who knows how long in front of you, on an expanse of sea and sands, on a park bench, on the grass of the park, to the sound of a brass band, against a pub wall, on the top and the back of a double-decker.

But all that aside, I go to the museum, eager to find The Kiss, eager to sit beside The Kiss, ready to form a reply. The Kiss once wrapped by the artist Cornelia Parker, her one-mile string bound around it … String someone later cut; this is what I think of as I enter the building. When I get to the museum, post-letter, eager to find The Kiss, eager to sit beside it – and maybe now, yes, maybe by then I was beginning to change direction with the words, maybe on the way to the museum I was already thinking of writing to you, composing a reply, pages already forming some little stories tapped out in time with my steps on my way through the park, along the tree-lined avenues, words already straying in your direction, along with the notion that I would have liked to copy your letter, to have blown it up as big as a billboard, carved it into oversized stones; your letter, illuminated over the front of The Quad like a Jenny Holzer: huge words

117

made from beams of light; to have copied the letter thousands of times, handed it out to strangers, to all the strangers you became; to have flown it from flagpoles, to have dropped it from aeroplanes, ticker-taped, to have wrapped buildings and post boxes with it, shrouded a cliff like Christo; yes, to have blown up the word hurt, and to have wrapped hurt around The Kiss like Cornelia Parker wrapped her one-mile string around it – this is what I think as I enter the building: The Kiss wrapped, seen anew, revitalised by string.

The museum, I can say, became a site of solace over the months between the letter's arrival in our home and the time when we flew off to Spain. The city's museum, where you can lose yourself in people, in paintings, in small cases filled with butterflies, the delicacy of a stuffed starling, the anthills alive with work, dead shiny bugs held in place like broaches on a coat lapel. The nearby Folk Museum where you can hide among the twists and turns of the buildings and gardens and outhouses, lose yourself in small stones and bakehouses, in stables and mills and dovecots, the spurs of a cock-fight, smoke escaping from chimneys, rows of houses, schools, chapel, all they had moved there, stone by stone, brick by brick.

Before that, I found myself running up the steps of the city's museum, fleeing our home, your words, daylight; fleeing the uncertainty of the outside by way of the grand white stone pillars, that huge solid entrance to the museum, a little flushed and out of breath when I first came looking for The Kiss. The first time, remembering they had moved it from the entrance and replaced it with the Little Drummer Boy; a little drummer boy that was actually rather large and old for a boy. I imagined it was upstairs, The Kiss, one of many bronze replicas. How they might move such lumps of metal fired my imagination. I would have liked to watch The Kiss in flight, carried by lines of suited men, like the Spanish carry the Virgin, candlelit, around the streets during *Semana Santa*. I never liked The Kiss, but now I wanted nothing more than to see it again close-up, to walk slowly around it, to touch. I even agreed with myself that if I found it I would write to you from there, a little opening, or a small beginning. That from the various sides of The Kiss I'd watch the responses of others, note down how a kiss could cause such a fire in the eyes, such a smile, such a grimace, such concentration; the bubbles blown in its direction, the sketches made, the circles taken, baby spit, not this, I could not share with others how my distaste for this very Kiss has now turned to a devoted faithfulness. I can only try to show how I now pledge to sit beside The Kiss with the warmth and defence of a mother.

No doubt I'll find it, if not today then soon, soon, that's what I tell myself, that I'll for sure find it. One day, come here and when I least expect it there it will be, there we will be, not me and you, but myself and others so soon in conversation around The Kiss, finding myself asking a crowd of strangers what they think of it. It gives me courage this Kiss, asking them what's the loveliest and the worse kiss they have given and received, the one that got away. Telling them the story of a woman kissed by the words of a stranger, lives kissed too hard ... Yes, there's a woman who kisses strangers; work of sorts, that's what I'll tell them, that's how she sees it. Not what you might assume at first, but rather a project of sorts, another artist. I forget her name... I'll mention that too, her name forgotten, that there's a woman who kisses strangers. Maybe we are all kissing strangers to begin with, how else? There's a woman who kisses strangers, and she approaches them asking, – Can I kiss you? Some of course are on top of her immediately, no hesitation; others are shy, suspicious, angry, running off, asking – What do you mean? Some are ever so politely heard saying – No thank you, as if they are turning down a free sample of *My Weekly*. Others hold their hands to their mouth and cannot go through

119

with the act; there are the usual giggles. Some blush but they let her kiss them anyway; some are very still and the kiss is not heard but for sure takes place. Others question her at length, finally give in, or walk off. A few point out the health hazards, wipe her and their mouth with a tissue, with the back of their hand. Some apply lipstick, some comb their hair, straighten their clothes, smile just before.

I'll ask them after some time, each of us with our own time and way of standing beside The Kiss, our own way of looking, I'll no doubt ask what's the worse letter they'd ever sent or received, the worse kind of threat, or bullying, or harm; what's the nicest letter they ever opened, or sent; how many paper kisses on average do they assign to the bottom of a page; how many letter kisses have they received to date. Hoping at this point they will not misconstrue my request as an offer to kiss, that I will escape any kisses they may wish to plant on a cheek or worse, an eye, a lip, another's spit wiped from a forehead or hand; the ones that talk that is, the ones that have the curiosity to rise to my question, to advance to a different kind of whiskered invitation; hoping that they will not misconstrue my request, walk off, give me that look, a wide birth.

Yes, all this runs through me in time with the sound my shoes make on the marble floors, the changes steps make crossing stone, marble, wood; whispers carry here. I find myself with a map, a map from which I still cannot locate The Kiss, a map I turn and turn again. My breath, my shoes rushing from room to room… Finally, somewhere near the silver and glass collection, almost blushing on The Kiss: the name, the request, the where now? The sound my question makes in the direction of the two attendants I follow, follow my call of – What have you done with it? What have you done with Rodin's Kiss…

I am told it has been stored away. They tell me without sentiment or favour. They linger only to say that for now it is hidden away in the basement. The basement. I feel it beneath our feet. How many marble pillars and wooden floors down, I don't ask; I only picture it hidden under throws, inside wooden crates, bound in new nails and ropes, dust and darkness. A sculpture I've had no interest in for so many years, a twisted embrace I've given no thought to at all, a Kiss I've walked by without more than a patronising glance over my spectacles; a Kiss I've only ridiculed, not given the time of day to. A Kiss that now drives me on from room to room, voices echo here as we move, as the pink light of the hall floods the faces of the museum attendants telling me that The Kiss is for now gone, moved, denied; for today at least I am left only with the shame of my own desire, bemused, thwarted, shifting from teasing indifference to an ache... Thinking again of the bracelet, way back, all of it unwanted, gold, the tiny diamond; all I've taken for granted and loathed in The Kiss, my distaste turned into disappointment, impatience, regret now forcing me on to the gift shop, forcing me to search out a small postcard, a Kiss too distant, too flat and badly lit, an acidic rather gaudy yellow backdrop that does not in any way satisfy...

~

Before the letter arrived, I was walking to work. Walking to catch the bus to take me to the writing group I taught each week. It was a lovely March morning; the park was filled with small children swinging and jumping and springing back and forth on the little metal horses. I was thinking about how my own boys used to love these horses, how it only seemed the other day that I was kneeling into the bark floor swinging them back and forth on those sprung mares. The trees looked particularly beautiful, lit up, bright greens and the beginning of spring, birds everywhere. We live in a city but still there are birds everywhere. The river meets the sea here and the gulls were that day especially wild and noisy, circling with the complete joy of themselves, with their freedom to move and fly, mocking what we could never know, all that they have up there with one another. Yes, as they swirled and dived and patterned the air without ever crashing into each other, the scene before me panned out – widescreen, all colour heightened, the way you feel when watching films, drowning in tones of light, expanses so wide it disorientates the eye, such a clarity, such attention to detail, such sharpness of sound.

I said to myself… Look at us, here we all are going about our day, not really bothering each other; smiling to myself at how well we manage to stick to our small patches of land, sides of the road and pavements, our stretches, our lines and circumferences and routes; how surprising it is that we walk around mostly tolerant of one another, unharmed; the freedom of the small island, the freedom of the West; recalling my driving instructor once laughing at me trying to negotiate the distance from my car to another car, from my wheel to the pavement – Well, you walk down the road each day and fail to collide with the curb and everyone around you; how come you do that, he said … it's the same thing, think less, feel more, he said, just feel the distance, feel the body of the car as if it is your own body easing through a door, along a road, feel the gap, let the proximity take care of itself. Look at us all, I said to myself that morning on my way to the bus, walking in the sun, taking this freedom for granted, this freedom to walk the streets without worry or threat, look at us all, keeping our distance, getting along, at ease with each other, with the day, early spring.

And it was on this same journey to work, on the bus now, almost there, almost at my destination. There I was, my face pressed to the glass window of the bus, dreaming from the window, dreaming of the book I was trying to write, *Windows*, dreaming of what we'd do that morning to come, what to write, dreaming that for once I'd like the bus to digress, to never reach its destination, to pass Go, collect £200 – by now surely with inflation added on – yes, passing Go. Go, I thought, fly like in the films, just once, like *Chitty Chitty Bang-Bang,* ET on the bike with the lad, yes, for once if the bus would only fly, take us all for a little jaunt…

It was then, to my right, that I saw the dead man. Or so I thought. I had no mind to check; it all happened so fast. The bus was in motion. It went by. I stared at him in a little park to my right – a small area of green in a dipped wooded backdrop, railings around, and him slumped on a bench in the distance, dead. I could have taken the next stop and checked – but I did not. Neither did the bus fly. Too soon I was sitting in my writing chair at work, explaining the theme for the morning, yet it plagued me all through the session, in which I'd asked them to begin *Thirteen Ways of Looking,* inspired by the beautiful poem of Wallace Stevens, his *Blackbird.* It was then instead that I found myself turning back to what I had seen that morning, in turn finding myself writing – Thirteen Ways of Looking at the Dead Man. I read it out, took my turn with the others. Explained what I had seen on my way to them. The others insisting, – You could have checked that the dead man was dead. – I know, I know. The guilt, when the day had begun so well. It was then that I pledged to go back and find him, pledged that on my way back I would for sure get off the bus and check. Make the small walk to the grass to the bench and get some help. But on the way back he was gone. You see what I mean. Days later, asking myself had I brought this on, like The Kiss, just weeks later, gone. Gone when you want it most. The dead man, surely a bad omen, surely the letter, something sparked from the idea I'd given wind to, the fragile notion of the freedom we all have. My ignorance that morning, with no inkling of what was to come; the same morning the dead man; the same week, the letter on its way.

THIRTEEN WAYS OF LOOKING AT A DEAD MAN ...

1. He was drunk. I was right to stay on the bus.
2. Deeply seated in a park, the man was for certain dead.
3. The dead man wore patent shoes, tight double bows.
4. People are already speaking of him in the past tense.
5. The brass buttons on the dead man's jacket shone in the sun. The jacket will be cleaned and pressed and taken to the charity shop. The same one he bought it from. The person who takes it there will not know this. The jacket will last another few deaths. The buttons will remain but the originals will fall, one by one will be replaced, and they won't match. The original buttons will be found by separate individuals and will always be in circulation on other clothes.
6. If there was a dog with the dead man, the dog said, *don't look at me;* the dog said, *fuck it, I'm out of here.* Yes, I am convinced there was a dog. People will say they had strong hair, dog and man, that you could not tell them apart. People will say that the dog did all he could but knew when to seize the moment; knew when to move on to more lively bodies, hands with sticks, whistles, finally a dog needs feeding and it's the living that are opening cans.
7. *I am who I am because my little dog knows me* [Stein].
8. I witnessed his death while inhaling another woman's face powder. None of the people with me on the bus verified his passing. Although I checked my watch, recorded my witness to be 10.51 am. He could have died much earlier or was maybe dying at the time.
9. Some die indoors. He chose spring, mid-morning. He'd arrived at the bench alive, while I was still at home washing

124

my hair. The dog later licked the dead man's shoe, then his hand, this was their last real contact before the dog took a final good sniff and made his exit.

10. Like me, the man was fond of shoes, but different styles.

11. Someone more decisive will remove the body. No one will claim the body. The dead man's watch will be stolen.

12. A borrowed line where it all began: *One man and a blackbird are one. I know too, that the blackbird is involved in what I know and do not know.* The blackbird made its entrance, settled in the tree; once the dog was gone, the bird sang sweetly over the body; later, it dug for worms, tugged at a lace by mistake – or just trying its luck.

13. I want the man to clear my conscience. To believe he lives and runs after the dog.

Frida's Story

I had been a teacher for almost thirty years when this began. In all that time I could count on one hand the verbal disagreements that I ever had with any member of staff at the schools I taught at. Indeed, there are people from the school I worked at prior to Monarvale that I still keep in contact with, who still give me a kiss or friendly greeting when I run into them.

I loved teaching. I am sure I could not have taught the blend "ch" or aspects of the number seventeen for years without spice.

I had been at Monarvale for over twelve years prior to a new principal arriving, a man with an enormous need to be liked, who was seen as a really *good bloke*. R was appointed around this time too.

R's behaviour to me in the first eighteen months or so was quite cordial – not especially friendly, but nothing out of the ordinary.

Over time, with the appointment of another teacher, P, R changed rapidly. She began to draw together a number of staff members and a wide range of parents and students. She had favourites and began treating some students, namely older boys, very badly.

She began stroking the Principal's ego constantly, eventually sharing confidences, stroking him physically; they even had pet names for each other.

My life at this time was busy, as I had a very difficult foster-child, a very depressed son, and a mum whose health was becoming frail.

With hindsight, there were lots of signs that R's behaviour had begun to change toward me. I can remember asking her a number of times what was wrong; I remember she was in my classroom each week and working with my kids (a great bunch of eleven & twelve-year-olds). Her answer was always offhand.

She would then be exceedingly charming to me for a few weeks and I would begin to relax. In my heart I truly believed that she could do me no harm.

Over time things became increasingly difficult with R and P. When I was Acting Principal for over a month, because the Principal was on compassionate leave, R and P used to turn their chairs in the opposite direction whenever I sat at the staff table. I began to hate the staff room and avoided it as much as possible.

R also cultivated a group of parents, mostly odd-bods with issues of their own.

I had a number of conversations with the Principal, raising concerns, and he basically told me I was paranoid.

Over a year I had hundreds of hang-up phone calls, but there was no pattern to them and I believed them to be related to my foster-child. There was also pornography delivered to my mum, drugging of my puppy, and our letterbox was firebombed. I only connected the dots after the event.

A really big event for the kids is their Year Six farewell, which is a dinner with speeches, pomp and ceremony. I was determined that my class would have a wonderful and memorable experience. The tradition had been to produce a yearbook. I wanted my class to have something very personal and so I designed a journal for each student. These were filled with memories, stories and personalised artwork for each individual student. A huge amount of work, but a journal that an ex-student recently told me she still reads.

R was helping the kids with their journals when she was in my classroom in the last few weeks. I tried to ignore her behaviour and had a wonderful evening with the kids and I got a huge surprise when the students from my class presented me with a journal that they had made for me.

The farewell was on Wednesday evening and the next day,

Thursday, was a lovely one with the kids bringing in their journals and sharing them.

When I went home there was the letter in my mail.

The hatred was palpable and it attacked every aspect of my life.

I remember that I had tears streaming down my face as I read it. I was on my own until Leo, my husband, came home. He didn't know what to say, my mum didn't know what to say, nor did my sons.

I rang the Principal but I was too incoherent to make sense.

Next morning after he had read it he was shocked and called a staff meeting. R and her friends were there.

I was sent home after speaking to a welfare officer and then I went to the police. The police said there would not be enough physical evidence to find out who had sent the letter but they tried to reassure me by telling me that the person would have done it before and was most probably a psychopath!

About a month prior to this, a parent had made an official complaint about an incident that had happened to her child. At the time we thought it was a genuine letter from the parent, and I didn't know that R had helped compose it and that she had a copy and that there had been a flurry of emails in relation to this in which she had been attacking my character.

My letter and the letter of complaint were both written in the same font, same language, and same writing style. Needless to say we believed it to be written by the parent. As you can imagine it was not possible for me to confront the parent.

Anyway, over the weekend I had a visit from a wonderful parent and also a friend who is a policeman. Talking to both of them enabled me to clarify my thinking. It was eventually proved that R wrote the letters but I didn't know who else was involved.

At this time I believed, as she wanted me to, that she was

having an affair with the Principal and had the whole school on her side.

We came back to school after five weeks' break and the Principal did nothing. To this day there has never been any discussion or repair or reaching out either to myself, other staff members or the parent body; each time I walked into the staff room there was whispering and then silence. P has always totally refused to speak at all about any of it. I had a parent-teacher meeting for my new class and as I was delivering the information I began looking around the room and I knew that there were a number of people sitting there who were involved. That took me away from school for over six months.

Today I am recovered and strong, but almost five years later just writing this stirs things. I realise that there will not be much sleep tonight.

Betty's account of Frida's story

I'm thinking back to that time when at school we found out about the letter Frida had received. There was a staff meeting and Frida, who had received the letter by post the day before, was absent because of her distress; this was a small five-teacher school. The Principal announced the news. I remember thinking he was enjoying it. The perpetrator of the letter, R, another teacher, a great favourite of his, was present at the meeting. But of course we didn't know this at the time, and because of its contents we believed it came from parents of the kids in her class. He didn't read out the letter, but said there was a copy in his desk which we could view. I was in the staff room with R and with P, a close friend of R's, when I said I'd like to read it, and she encouraged me to go and get it from the desk. She watched me reading it, and my shock. I actually said, 'I think this person is a thick-wit.' But because I was ignorant of her complicity, I wasn't watching the reaction on her face.

The whole thing went on for another two and a half weeks, during which there was much speculation as to who exactly had sent it. Many parents were suspects. Eventually, it was the parents who worked out who sent the letter, and they contacted the Principal who said at another staff meeting that he wished 'they [the parents] hadn't reported this.' He was eventually forced, with obvious reluctance, to confront R, and then she was gone, denying any involvement. No job, but no repercussions either. Had she been innocent, she would undoubtedly have stood her ground and protested. She didn't. And he wasn't going to do a thing about it. It finished and was never discussed again.

On re-reading the letter, I was overcome by its tedious contents. The woman herself is a monumental bore and the letter reflects it, but the words had a violence.

My aunt told me today that she received an anonymous

phone-call from a woman who accused Auntie's daughter of having an affair with her husband, a man who used to deliver goats to the property they lived on. Aunty ended the conversation by saying, 'I think you are an awful nanny-goat!' No more was heard.

The other examples you are putting in the book are disturbing. Can you believe them all?

it will give me and my collegues even greater pleasure when we meet up with you...

Cowardly, Bridget says. When we take her a copy of the letter, when she reads it quietly to herself. Bridget is our Trauma Counsellor, so-called. The one we finally agreed on. The one recommended to us when the woman who works with visualisations – no quips intended – couldn't see us both. It's just that En and I insist that we have to be seen together, that it affects us both, the letter. Even though we are sceptical of seeing anyone at all. Despite this, I found myself ringing around after we rejected The Quad's offer of in-house experts.

Believe me, I would love to be able to tell you the order of things, to give some narrative satisfaction, some sense of coherence, but after your letter arrived what kind of reply was possible? The absurdity of my writing this to you at all, to someone I know nothing of, my voice sent out in the direction of an imagined ear, floating, oversized, enormous fleshy lobes I hang onto, pinna, ear canal, entering through minute delicate hairs – let's hope you're groomed, no wax; that you've scented just behind your ear with a dab of cologne. Or am I stuck in the wrong sense organ, surely a letter back to you is addressed to both eyes, eyes rubbing sleep away, eyes that hold no memory, how else to get through all the drudgery and disorder an eye has to deal with in a day but to rub it out, water it down, twenty-five blinks per minute, 13,104,000 per year. Imagine ... what colour are your eyes?

– That's what such a letter does, Bridget says: it causes disorder to strike the day. There we are some weeks after the letter in Bridget's small dark room, sunlight held at bay. The room lit by a small candle over the fireplace. The gesture of the candle is what you might expect yet is somehow comforting: the flickering, the intimacy. The room such a contrast to the fortress

132

our home has become: Quad business, dark suits, briefcases placed beside black-laced shoes – office-wear then a regular occurrence around our kitchen table, the emergency meetings to discuss types of action, the adjustments to the plans for our safety, publicity, strategy, police business, agendas, suspicions, leaks and statements.

Bridget's sofa, the tea, the clock, the window behind us, the armchairs where En and I sit facing her, turned into each other, our six knees, the sound of soothing music somewhere in the distance again makes me smile. I decide to put any cynicism aside, to give myself over to the security we feel in this room, the comforting calm of the place, Bridget's lilting Northern Irish accent. Somehow the fact that she had come from such an unsettled homeland, worked in the thick of what became referred to as The Troubles, eased me, gave me confidence in her, even if our own troubles seemed nothing in comparison to what she must have witnessed in her past – though I knew for sure that we were under a type of siege.

No denying that with distance, as now I begin to piece all I have written to you together, doubt raises its narrow eyes over the whole sorry incident. I find myself again apologising that compared to others' experiences this incident seems now so slight, so insignificant. Only yesterday for instance, on the radio – I tuned in specifically because there was a programme about harassment. Immediately imagining a thread, some connection or understanding, as for sure, whatever varied and conflicting labels people attach to the gesture of the letter, it is at the very least what you'd consider harassment. The woman being interviewed on the radio had been stalked. There was also a police officer in the studio, who specialised in the crime of stalking. She agreed that it wasn't being taken seriously enough. That no one knew how to handle such matters. They often see it as *domestic*, she said; no more than idle threats that go nowhere. Ignore it, people tell you. The woman in this case had befriended *a rather strange character at work*, a man a bit at odds with everyone, a loner; she felt sorry for him, took an interest in him, tried to help. In the end he made following her his full-time job. He even managed to get a set of her house keys copied, not unusual they say, and he let himself in while she was out, would rearrange things in her home, and small personal objects would appear on her office desk from her bedroom. She left a Post-It in her kitchen reminding her to buy bread, and when she got home the bread was waiting for her. He put listening devices in her bed. Later he finished a very short prison sentence, came out, changed his name to the name of the woman's ex-husband, went on to murder another woman he'd stalked in the same way.

Ask:

How in comparison can I speak of this, of you, to you, spend so much of my time imagining, casting my mind out; what scraps form from what's left of a letter now hidden somewhere, forgotten. For sure you did not copy our keys, put listening devices into our bed, the bed where I first learned of your words; for sure you did not buy or make me bread while we were out and leave it on our table. Yes, talking of bread, with the passing of time is it easy to admit that I have a tendency to stretch out these tales like yeast blown from the mouth, to feel the bubble and rise swell up well beyond the mixing bowl, to wonder now if I am making my own wholemeal out of this, a puff pastry, a baker's dozen, when really in hindsight, in the kitchen and oven light of a late morning, when your letter came there were months of worry, alarm, literally and metaphorically, and then what ... You and I having no tea, no clue, no idea, no buttered buns with jam, not a damn inkling of what is now, what was then, what is any longer between us ...

You could say that for now I've too quickly abandoned

134

En and myself in Bridget's room, that the candle is burning low, that the music has looped back on itself and repeats every soothing tune; you could say that the hour a week we have had with Bridget over some months is already well and truly up and what have we said to one another yet?

I can say that this is how it continues for weeks.

This is how it went by and on…

En and me and Bridget once a week in the small dark room, with the chairs facing one another, ours south, hers north – we always took the same positions, En to my right, Bridget in front of us on her small sofa, our knees almost together across the divide … until finally En got another job. We gave back all the alarms, and *the rest I have said already* – that we went to Spain for a needed break, *yes, yes;* that we took the three boys, that all was well, we felt safe there, we felt free again, we were sound there, happy, content – *don't overdo it* – that from there I began to write to you, each day, in the morning, the first morning I wrote…

Birds flew the length of a wall.

That's it in an eggshell…

Is this our wood – the wood you spoke of…

When you think you are out of the woods but aren't. When you least expect it, there we'll be…

A year later, are we still in the wood or out…

Are we all permanently wood-bound?

I go back to Bridget. It is a year on and so much is forgotten; but how else would we live other than by forgetting so much? I go to Bridget so she can give me back some memories. Like that dream I had once in which I was living in a world where all our memories had been denied, in a world where the only way we could escape the present tense was to have other people read our memories for us, the way people try to look into the future, pay people like tarot shufflers, mind-readers, tea-leafswillers – to turn to what vain versions?

A year on, I am on the way to Bridget to say there is nothing substantial enough to remember or write about. It is a sieve of a reply, holey cheese, smoke rings – not mine; no more than false starts and promises, a tea-stain of a letter aimed at where, what, whom. Still, I'm on my way to see Bridget, realise that I am early, pass half an hour in a café writing up some questions to *Ask Bridget*, which makes me laugh and think of *Warhol*, his *Ask Bridget* reply to any question put to him. I dawdle around gift shops and buy Bridget a bunch of flowers from the florist. As the woman wraps them she tells me they are renunculas. En will later tell me this is from the same family as the buttercup, pink under Bridget's chin – what does pink reveal? – two women sharing a story of a letter. I take her renunculas, different shades of pale pink as delicate as the memories of that time you wrote. We make tea and the room is familiar and I am glad to be back, glad to speak of your letter in the past tense, glad to settle back into the same seats we always used: Bridget on the small sofa, me opposite in the left-hand chair, En's to my right, empty.

Bridget's account of the letter

None of you were in your usual patterns. Only your kitchen, the table was in place, your hiding place, but En was home from work, and you weren't even listening to the radio as you always do each day. To begin with you hardly went out. All the normal little things that make up a life were cast aside.

Coming here each week was like a secret place that no one knew about. You couldn't trust The Quad any more. What happened threatened people most precious, that was the biggest part of it, and that En carried the letter around with him in his pocket, over his heart. I remember that vividly, that he carried the letter in his pocket everywhere and you asked him not to, you asked him to put it somewhere off his person. And there he was, asking me, – Do you want to see it? The letter. There I was questioning, Will I see it; should I see it, and then En handing it over to me, to keep, as if it were going to ignite.

The letter you can't even put your hands on now; the letter you changed the name of, from Letter to Fairy Cake. Do you remember, by the time you came to see me, how sick you were of saying *the letter, the letter*. It was a brief flutter, you might say; no more than the first thing that came into your head, maybe the first day we met here. And I know you said that you rarely bake cakes but somehow when it happened you had the urge to burn the letter in your Aga while alongside you were making a tray of small cakes, to take the small cakes in your hand like Proust's *petite madeleine* dunked in the tea, only to decorate the thing with sprinkles and hundreds-of-thousands and candied fruits on top of thick pink icing, letter and cake alike, to ice, toast and glitter, candle and light. Actually on the way here today I passed some shops, noticing in the window of one an entire display of ceramic and wax fairy cakes; enough to make me laugh, enough to make me go inside, pick up a glazed

137

cake, turn it in my hands, consider buying it for you, smile to myself, feign a bite, a sniff. When only this morning a friend was telling me how her partner, on just hearing that the cancer she had was treatable, to celebrate, her body still filled with chemo, had wanted to do something nice, wanted to treat herself – I imagined a holiday, an outfit or two, a wardrobe, a change of life – instead she went out to buy herself some cake tins; she wanted to go home and bake some cakes. That happens. It's so simple. And what also happens is that often the perceived threat, the one in our imagination, sometimes that becomes worse, worst-case scenario. Not that I am comparing actual threats with perceived, but it is really important to say that perceived or written threats feed the imagination, the imagination flying around the devil and back. Even if the person names himself it can still be difficult, because he could find someone else to come after you, so everyone you come across is a potential attacker. It could happen at any time.

At the time of the letter, I told you not to watch TV – remember your habit of late-night news each night? Because of what happened your antennae is going and if you do see the news suddenly it is all pointing back at you. Do you remember at the time that one of the main news items the same week En got the letter was about a vicar who had been stabbed by some young man who was stalking him, threatening him, maybe anonymously to begin with, I can't recall how well he knew the man, if at all, when he began receiving threats, it was never made clear, but I clearly recall that the vicar was found by his wife in the church grounds, there he was dying in his wife's arms, and that fed into your whole narrative.

Part of it is the person choosing you, an anonymous other saying: I am coming after you; and in that moment when the person writes the letter and makes the threat he or she is of course thinking of you, and then what? Days later, when you have received the words, when you can think of nothing else, what then is that person thinking about? Maybe not thinking of you at all any more ... and how to get the person you are working with to see that. Maybe that's it – the person writing gets rid of it all with that one letter; there is no more, the author exhausts him- or herself in that single act of writing and then maybe doesn't even remember it, maybe then he or she forgets all that was done and said. I remember that was the bit that you couldn't get your head around, that you were both so full of the person who wrote the letter, that person completely entered your lives and every little corner of it so it was all you could think about, and there I was saying that he may not even be thinking about you any more. How can that be possible? As if the letter is a kind of marriage certificate.

It reminded me of when I was living in Northern Ireland. We'd get graffiti written, written on walls, and pavements coloured, and flags everywhere, and different kinds of written words all over, but also heard, made clear when intimidation would happen, where we lived identified, writing left on the outsides of houses and arrows saying, This way to ... So there you'd be, walking home, and just about to put your key into the door and there'd be a different kind of letter waiting, written to you in large sweeping strokes. And yes, what do you do then? Do you go and get something to wash it off? Do you get rid of it?

That reminds me that you once told me that someone had thrown an egg at your window, at the window in front of where you work at your desk. At the time you said that Hugo had been involved in quite a difficult friendship with a boy he went to school with, when they were about ten years old. The kid he'd befriended, or who had befriended Hugo, came from a pretty chaotic home, and one day he'd just walked around the table at school while everyone was quietly working, the teacher was chalking something on the board, and he'd punched Hugo randomly, out of the blue, dislocating his jaw. The shocking thing was that there was no warning, no name-calling, no prior sign, no argument, nothing – and Hugo thinking that the boy was just walking toward him to tell him something. The boy was very calm. The police were involved; you had to be interviewed and filmed behind a two-way mirror – something to do with Hugo's age. Months later, you said… It was bonfire night or around that time when all the kids were letting off rockets and squibs and you'd got an egg thrown at the window – which happens. But you'd noticed the gang of kids run off and one of them was the boy who had dislocated Hugo's jaw. You said that you'd sat there and stared at the egg for ages, feeling quite threatened by it, by seeing the boy again, by his proximity and his gang and you felt worried for Hugo, what it meant. But it was an egg, it was ridiculous but it's what it represents, the violation of the house, that border. Like the kids around the table in school; their sides, my side, your side, the image of the child suddenly quietly getting up and walking around the table… The author of the letter getting up and walking to the writing desk, to the typewriter, to the post box. The egg on the window was nothing, but I remember you said that it stayed there for ages, as to wash it off felt … I don't know … really stupid! But not really, because to wash it off would be to engage with it in some way; on one level it's taking it away and on another it's engaging with it physically, making it more real… I don't think this is unusual, not at all. We can freeze as much around these things as you did with the letter… But with the egg, if you'd asked people what they would have done, they'd probably all say, Well, I'd wash it off, love…

I remember I told you to place pots of thyme outside the door, and you did, almost tongue-in-cheek but you liked the idea that it would keep you safe, yes, herbs, all those old traditions and old wives' tales, but at times we all want the reassurance of

140

a rabbit's foot, we buy charms and the like ... And one evening, someone stole one of the pots. The nerve! And you saw it as a sign when really it was just someone just taking your pot! But for a moment you find yourself seeing it as an extension of the threat, wondering has the person been around, is he telling you something, is this the start of something more ... this little invasion into your front yard and so close to your house. For some that would have less impact; for some people it would be other things that worry them, like other people's music ... those kinds of environmental sounds and things like the graffiti that reminded me of home, of childhood, what some would class as a violation, others would not.

It's a little bit like verbal bullying, which is dismissed as if it's only physical violence that can damage us ... back to the letter carried in En's pocket, but carried inside us too because in that sense the letter was an act of bullying. The arguments at The Quad about what to call this letter, how to categorize it, name it; I guess we all get told things each day, that we are this or that ... words that make up their minds about us, affect us, hurt us; *he said, she did*, you hear it all the time, in conversations everywhere, so much misunderstanding, impossible name-calling; body language. I guess the letter was an exaggeration of that, pointed very specifically in language toward and at your home.

I didn't have some master (or mistress) strategy when you came to see me. You and En were both static. Your every day had become focused on that one letter, particular sentences in it, when as a family you have a whole bunch of stories and other kinds of letters and postcards, delicious postcards, different kinds of stories that became swept aside, forgotten about. Thinking of postcards – as soon as you go away the first thing you want to do is to share that, to send words home to loved ones. You could also see the person who wrote the letter as telling his story, or her hurt... And I know you thought that many times, about the other person's side and story, and maybe you still do; that maybe that person – the author/s of the letter – and you and En as a family, were all finally different kinds of victims of the institution, as The Quad remains the same, goes on untouched, whatever people come and go everyone is disposable there. In this way the institution of work directly invaded your home, your day-to-day life, how you slept at night, how you opened the curtains, the jolt you felt when you heard the mail arrive, when someone rang the bell, that's a fierce intrusion. Maybe that's why the letter should have been aimed at The Quad, not at En. But from the author's point of view, how do you begin to attack a huge institution like that? But still, the letter was an inappropriate way of sharing that other story, I'd say; I'd say, Keep that kind of response to yourself, honey, find other ways.

The letter as it was has changed now. It's gone. Some things remain, like some of the door furniture; most things have moved on, almost all signs of defence. And of course part of my job was to minimise it, to play it down, because when the letter arrived it was growing heads and legs and arms and so now you are left with ... *what was that all about?* The fear and the leaving it behind, both those stories are true.

I remember at the time you said that a friend had wanted to write you a letter, to write you something beautiful to let you know she was thinking of you, but she was worried how you'd all react to getting a letter in the mail, for a moment not knowing whom it was from. So something dear in that form, in that address and gesture, became impossible, all those letters that couldn't be sent any more, all those lost unsent letters never read.

Day Pages – Spain

The Mountain of the Dead Woman has two peaks. As you approach via the Carattera Penota, the first peak is 2003 metres, the second 2193, and a third peak, En says, is 2009 metres … written beneath the words on the map. Is it that the dead woman is simply the name of the mountain, or is it that a dead woman is buried inside? On the map the mountain looks no more than a little smudge, a mistake. Did I stray too far from the story of Michael where I began with the right-hand pages, did I move to a mountain too quickly? What could have become of Michael, Michael who has now become a mountaineer – sure-footed, the steadiness of a goat, the sound of a bell carried across a morning.

The roads all look the same to her, to The Mountain of the Dead Woman. – It's not easy, En repeats, to approach her, to know the best way, it's very complicated. He checks and rechecks the map. And so he will continue to do, every ten minutes or more, as we stutter on. Stop at a deserted railway, imagine living beside a dead railway. – It's not easy, he says, to disturb someone's early morning solitude. In the half-sun on his balcony the man who lives beside what was the old station is at a table writing the same lines over and over … *It's not easy* … We ask the way, we blunder on, the map already open, and he leaves his unfinished replica line and rises happily, now raising his hand and pen to his eyes, explaining that it's not this station we need but another station that is close by. In the shade of the acacia that has grown irregularly we ask again for directions to her, to The Mountain of the Dead Woman. We ask the men drinking outside the second station: – Where next? The bar is called Station Bar! A conversation opens up about the stork who unfolds her wings and decides to go nowhere; her nest is built in four uneven layers that resemble a lopsided hat of which she is the plume. The hat is made on top of a neat brick stack some thirty feet over the station bar, stack and stork holding the egg for an ending.

The men redirect us and we see that the mountain is so close now that we could hardly know that we are already upon her; no longer able to make out her shape, made up of forestry and picnickers, twisted roads and paths that run through and up to her, the odd white bony cow sitting at the roadside. Luke and D hanging from the back window to film the cows. A disused outdoor pool we circle, broken pool ladders still visible, a deep blue rectangle covered now in weeds, filled with green slime where only the stray dogs dare to venture, until the road ends and a red gate stops everything. A woman sits at a small table on the other side of the gate absorbed in her crossword or whatever letter she has received and is writing her reply to. She takes her time to show any interest in us, if indeed there is interest at all, as we all pile out to ask if she can let us through. Then she reacts just enough to tell us that the entrance to the mountain is locked. A man opposite, on our side of the gate, seems to want to keep her company. He, unlike her, has no table. He stands and shows his obvious interest in her, like the intent interest that she shows in her papers, her letters, her books. I believe she wants him to leave – or rather, doesn't care if he stands there all day or not; his attention to her will not change the amount of time or favour she will offer.

When we get to the entrance to our mountain, she tells us that no one is allowed to enter either driving or on foot, in case people set fire to her, our dead woman; only a gate between us but enough to prevent us walking onto her, to know why she is so named. As we drive back I say that it seems apt after all that we are not allowed to enter, to see her, to walk upon her, that we are left simply to speculate on the possibility of a fire which could be started from our curiosity alone – we have no more to ignite her with than that. As we drive away, I feel the loss of her. Into the distance. We leave her some hundreds of metres back, a body of white rock rising from a blanket of green spruce. Now we return to her feet, stop the car, take a good look back at her, shade our eyes as her legs come into view, the mound of her belly, hands folded across her chest. Hugo says he sees her now and points. One by one we all point too and shout out, – Look! Look up at her coming into being, hazy in the sun, her chest like an open rib cage. Not hands but ribs. An open hole that big, where she was killed. – She's been shot, D says. – A hole, Luke says, where someone took out her heart. It is then that we see her fully. Her sleeping body as we drive further west, our heads twisted back to see the last of her. Further speculation about how we could have driven past her so many times this week and not seen her like this before, not seen more than her name. A green blanket beneath her waiting to be ignited, a pyre waiting to send her off as if she died at an angle – from here you can see how she slopes in death, falling away, laid out, head elevated. We gaze up at her corpse. Stop again. Photograph her as best we can, knowing we are too far away and she will not easily be duplicated.

Later we will return and eat lunch beneath her: *gigantes*, iced soup, *paella*, fish with *mariscos*, *flan y natilla*. The waiter will tell us that in winter she is shrouded in snow, blue with cold, preserved in ice, that animals sleep in her closed eyes like dreams, goats curl up in her belly, slide from her feet and continue on … until spring comes to her lips again. He says that no one is sure why she died. We forget what we are seeing and we think about this dead woman we have all begun to believe in. How does a mountain look forty years old when she has been there for hundreds of years alive and dead, she has a woman's hips. – Maybe she died in childbirth, the waiter says. D says that we read too much into rock. Now you've seen her, the way she shimmers beside the Rio Frio, there is no way back to unseeing.

We return to what has become our temporary home, more at home than in the home we left. We drive home and I daydream about the job of a gatekeeper at the entrance to a mountain. The lone woman and a table, a small folding chair. Imagine this job, guarding hundreds of orange butterflies, a red gate and a mountain for company. The keeper, her day mostly unpeopled. A living made and a lifetime spent keeping vigil, preventing cremation. They grow old together, keeper and mountain; one outlasts the other and the next and the next. Last rites go on for always. Who watches over whom? Does the keeper sometimes wander up to see more of her, when it's quiet? In what language do they speak, and of what, those two, when the wind blows out the forbidden matches she carries in her keep-safe-pocket, the strike of laughter refusing all she says, all the lies between them allowed, for she is on the side of the mountain. Because we are always this side of the gate, she says, this side of fire and death.

~

Writing up the story of the Mountain of the Dead Woman some days ago brought back a story that my father told me when I was very young. As I write this I can no longer remember if I made it up. When I phone him to check, he tells me I have not.

Yes, lying out frozen in the snow, the stranger I've carried with me. Try to forget that I cannot forget her story.

Wintering ... A word I first came across in a poem by Plath.
One story triggering another
Wintering

It was evening when Father told me about her for the first time, the nurse; how they'd returned her home, Father said, her body a white glitter parcel on a Christmas Eve gone by. Yes, the story of a woman I barely knew comes back to me: there were other renditions. This time the stars were out, me on my father's shoulders, nine feet between us then, together we formed a star of sorts beneath a star of sorts, moving through midnight. No, eleven's the hour, just before, unsteady steady man. You have to give up on shoulders when you grow; when you grow into a woman there are no more shoulders to climb.

Everything snowed that night, Father said, white as her body carried back home in a small meat wagon, her body a glitter parcel silent under the swaying hocks. Carrion: sounds like *beloved*, sounds like *carry on with the tale*. Know she was happy for a moment, he said, just before, just before she was lost. The storm came. This is how it was, a blizzard of snow, disorienting all sense of her path. The ache of muscle, the fear that caused her to sit down just for a while, lie down a while, she told herself; just lie down for a few minutes, no more than that. Maybe later a shape her body made in the snow, a rabbit or an angel, last words she patterned, her arms fanned into a blizzard, where dreaming turns to sleep.

Where we later stood she lay, he said. Stood to take on a mountain, searching for her body with our long sticks lancing the snow. Way back nothing is as it was, we suddenly forget all direction, like her, the mapping is all lost. The mountain spreads itself large and mean and she makes a decision to lie down in the snow. A moment that changed something in us all. Something she hadn't foreseen; she had not imagined that a mountain could mean it, could change and withdraw all direction, could call on her to stop a while, bewildered, hush now.

The blankets were extra thick that night, Father said, that night when they carried her body home in the meat wagon, stiff as the Christmas pigs that hung over her. All following close by, you child, on your father's shoulders, not now, but years

147

back, years on as he retold the tale; a question of mood, the sheepskins in our beds electric that night, sheep lit up by degrees beneath us. We, dark-wrapped, as we returned what we didn't like of her face turned over in the snow, her face that wouldn't leave us. The damp mittens she'd pulled free just before the hat worked itself loose, the fluid of dizzy creatures, eyes hard staring at the blue pines that gave no grace.

I have no bees, he said, unexpected – years back, reminding me of the bee he told me was present when they found her body, absent now, a single bee in winter, is that even possible? No one answered. I have only a memory of the bee that flew over her face, Father said, her face caught smiling in the snow like that and God knows she was happy at the last.

I don't have her name, he said. She was a nurse; yes, that much I confess, and that the colour of her hair alone was dark, wet curled, that much he confirmed. And that the women collected branches to adorn her body. The next day the women lit fires. Father said that some knitted while they kept vigil over the body, they knitted cosies for the teapots – he's teasing, adding things in, making it up now! There's always tea with this story, he'll say, a good reviving cup of tea – every season, every crisis, every death. Years pass, tea golden in tall glasses burning our fingers.

The women picked branches for her, branches they collected out of respect. And I'd think of the women picking branches, branches filled with white berries from the women who cared for her that night, next morning; all those who watched over her body, standing, admiring what they had arranged. They'd have got up early, he said, the women who cared for her; they'd have lit a fire. They'd have done nothing else but watch over her body thawing out, preparing her return to the earth. For the ground and sky accept all we offer, Father said. They did nothing else but listen for the first crackles. Placing damp clothes, theirs, hers, of no use, before the fire. Last night's damp clothes that picked up the smell of wood smoke, each winter after that, each fire, the sugar to help the coals flare. The salt sorrow calls up. Wintering I have carried her with me, a story that won't shift, forty years on, the stories we'll go on to repeat over tea, bread, slices of marzipan.

You have no bees, I'll say, out of keeping, an odd turn of phrase no one will now understand, years on in another country, late evening, nothing's in flight, only the stories passed on to a new generation, to Hugo, to D and Luke; night crickets, the hum of a tractor, tea and the stories we continue to share and we are glad of it.

Some weeks before your letter, I received a very different kind of letter from a young woman I'd only briefly met.

A letter asking me to take part in a collection of writing she was gathering. A letter asking people to write about something they feared most. At the time, neither the young woman nor I had any knowledge that the letter from you would soon be on its way. At the time I received her letter, I could think of nothing. My fear was that I had no fear. M asking, – Well, what would you do if at night an enormous spider crawled over the bed? I told him that I wanted to think of something original, beyond the usual arachnophobia, moths, snakes; my father's fear of frogs that would cause my constant spring supply of frogspawn to mysteriously disappear as soon as there was the slightest sign of a leg in the jar. Until your words came our way, what innocence; ask myself, Is it you I fear or the idea of you … as Hugo always jokes… It's not me you love, Mert, Mother, it's just the idea of me.

After her question, despite it all, it began to preoccupy me – that before your letter arrived I could come up with no tangible fear. I asked around. Most people's, outside the clichéd rats, bats and moths, were also what you'd expect: fear of public speaking, getting fat, eating in front of others, fear of doctors, using public toilets, crossing bridges, wasps, death. Only later did fear then become something brought home and petted like the new pups Father would often carry in unannounced, pups not yet weaned, pups who would whimper and shake during the night, their abandonment causing their fear to multiply, to locate, find their way into the darkness of your room, calling you back from the edge of dreams. After your letter's arrival I would wake most nights at whatever hour your words would call me back from sleep. I'd go, as usual, to get myself some tea from the kitchen downstairs. A creaky decent down the stairs

150

only exaggerating the silence of the house, only exaggerating the possibility that you'd be there watching, waiting, worse, smiling, back at the bottom. Yes, there I was in mid-flight on the stair, my leg held high, hovering, remembering that before you came, for as long as I can remember, one of my biggest fears was that I would forget how to walk.

How could I forget. This came back as I anticipated you, hesitated as I often do when faced with the same dark sloped run of carpet. There I was suspended on what you could say was the first or the twenty-second step, depending on whether you're going up or down. And just as I was beginning my decent I even noticed what kind of socks I had chosen to slip on for a moment's warmth, all that in a second, a second in which even the wallpaper caught my attention, the seams not quite joining, a stray handprint, a blue mark, a sharp C someone tried to erase and didn't succeed – all that took my attention, and then I thought of all I cannot remember … or yet know …

First steps … Last steps …

What could be more frightening than to see my leg held pre-descent, refusing to move, suspended for a moment, my hesitation pulling me into some uncertain future – a future that came upon me in a second: a future in which I saw myself wearing not the socks I'd normally pull on at such times but, as an old lady, wearing sensible hooked velvet booties. I could see that in the future I wouldn't bend so well to take the needed precautions over laces. I'd revert to my childhood temperament. What I found and held onto one day fell away the next. Maybe it was winter in that foresight, a vision of the future more like a memory of something already lived and known. It might have been December inside a spring memory when I descended the stairs, seeing my usual smooth leg, flexed muscle, now an old wrinkled thigh hovering on the stairs, puffy ankles held inside a step untaken. I saw the self to come, layered in wool, cardiganed, layered stale with the night turns; to exaggerate, I add now in my address to you a small bonnet.

And I looked up and thought … I am old now here in this vision … I am old now and the family has gone. En passed away, and the boys long left. And in that moment I watched myself trying to descend the stairs as a widow, as a woman who had long ago raised her children. I was on my way to get a drink, something warm and dilute, for you had pulled me out of bed again so late. I had almost forgotten any notion of words, letters – until it all came rushing back, pulling me from the warmth of the feathers, up and already speaking to you, then, now, my hesitation, my right leg shaking a little from the fear and the stammer of not being able to take its turn and move to the lower step. My right leg stiffening, contorted, heavier than I remembered when I remembered my hand reaching out for the rail to my left to steady my indecision. I do this always, even now as I tell you this, I see my hand reach out to grip the rail, to tell you again *that this is my fear* – my long-rooted fear – that I will forget how to walk; that forgetting how to walk could inevitably lead to a fall, a fall in words, or maybe a fall that will naturally result in a cry filled with words, in a voice I may not yet recognise, a cut or two, worse – the possibility of a tangled corpse.

And then the thought of the trouble I first had with walking came back, as well as the trouble with getting started on telling you this. What fears we all have, your letter aside, what fear is upon us these days, those days, the days to come, the trouble I first had getting started with walking. A place, a time, an event I have no recollection of, when as a child I had taken those very first steps, arms, mine, Mother's, open in doubt, in expectation. Of course I have seen my own children start with steps, with words I remember well. I could tell you the story of when and where they first gaggled towards me, chests leading, arms flapping open, how we tried to call them to us, catch them under the tree … a tree planted by their father. It was summertime, both times, or late spring at least, but I remember the feeling of the tree and the heat, of letting them go, running ahead: it was necessary that we let them try. As for my own first moves, I have no recollection. I could go and ask. I could call my mother now, if I could find a way to move from that step, but not now in the middle of a tale, such a long night, nights stretched out after your words came; who would expect such a letter, such a question at such an hour, any hour: where did I take my very first steps? When and where did you take yours? For now I feel safe and sound just knowing that somehow I *did* walk alone, that there *was* a first time, despite some horrid trace that remains when I watch those wild beasts or the calf or the colt make those first messy attempts toward the vertical. I saw *Bambi* – you'll laugh – my first film with Mother; maybe yours too, maybe we have more in common than we could ever know. Above all else I remember that moment on the ice. Watch always from a place of immunity. Thankfully I was not like Bambi, I was given more time to make my ascent, a year, many months or more before I was found pulling myself up against the tug of gravity. Lying comfortably to begin, supine. The luxury of food carried to my mouth for a while, left to lie in my own waste, left to feel the ground for reassurance before being forced UP – UP like we all are. Was it a natural curiosity for fresher air that caused me to leave ground, shoes, and legs? Was it simply a fear of being stepped on, a fear that surely lifted me up toward my mother's face, to sniff the air, to balance precariously on each foot, to lock my knees, a type of early stilt walker – but this is nothing you don't know. We have all had to do this, to consider this, even if in retrospect. Who can remember that time? – we all have our fears, hollow sounds. All this while my leg, my right leg was still suspended, held there still on the twenty-second step.

Day Pages – Spain

Patterns soon emerge no matter how far from home we are: dust patterns, routine patterns, different brooms taking on different jobs, one broom like a witch's. There's something in the rhythm of sweeping, the gathering of dust, orange pips, dead flies; I watch En sweep – does he still think of you? I watch him but won't ask. Stray thoughts collected into a dustpan with a long handle. He keeps a clean house. The way men always claim the barbecue. My father would do the same. Maybe you also cook a good garden sausage, sweep, the brush lifting up our feet. The long-handled pan with the little flap that lifts for the dust, closing on the dust. I watch En sweep. Think that it would be hard for you to hurt him if you saw him this way. If you saw the way he tends to plants. At home, the way he will pot up herbs for me. Herbs to keep us safe, herbs we leave by the front door. The way his fingers press soil into pots. The way he turns the plant in the pot. Waters them in. Stands back and says, – Look! Looks at it this way and that. The sound the trowel makes on the stone path when he plants in tiny grasses, sun on the delicate shoots. – Look what I've planted between the stones. It looks nice and the tortoises would like it – if we had any, that is. It's pretty … the word *pretty* once again between us, between the taps of the trowel. Promising not to trample between the stones, the shoots. – Be careful not to harm them, he says. Tread carefully. Carefully spraying the trees with water. The way he asks if I would like some tea. How he taught me the names of trees and in turn I taught him the names of teas, a garden in themselves: Rose Pu-erh, Chrysanthemum, Honey Orchid, White Peony. Maybe instead we'd all laugh if you could see En in the garden tending to tiny pieces of grass. Carrying a pot of tea. I don't know why it's funny. Maybe it's the conciliation, the rhythm of conciliation, gentle repetitive strokes, fingers brushing earth, sweeping earth over tiled floors. Pouring from the pot. The smell of jasmine, the concentration planting or pouring takes, the simplest of things that allow the mind to wander, to rest.

A man on the radio talking about war crimes; the average age of dead world-war veterans was twenty-five. If they'd only swept instead, worn an apron, potted herbs. Would this have stopped you – if he'd answered the door to you wearing an apron with a pocket, carrying a gravy-spoon?

What can I tell you? – that he leaves small notes for me on the table when he gets up early for work: *Don't forget the prunes have stones.* That I photographed him once, En, he was sitting against a white wall, or rather it was me who placed him there. Projected an image he'd taken once when he lived in Zambia. An image he'd taken of a mangled car, abandoned, no bodies, nothing macabre, just the car wreck, the wheel in the air; the mangle of metal. I projected the image onto his body. You could still recognise him if you looked closely. He was wearing his trousers, no shirt. It was decent but what you might call my peculiar period. The image, twisted metal, his face imprinted with the tyre.

If your greatest enemy was holed up with you for months in a room with prunes and aprons, stitches, potting soil, a broom, little notes, in what direction would the two of you finally face?

– Your father, I say again to Luke, knows the names of trees, the Latin names too. He's taught me over the years to remember, to recognise and pronounce the names of trees. We'd walk around the park, our country, this country, the woods, the fields, the cities, the back alleys, and riverbanks and we'd call out the names of trees. We stand beneath trees looking up until we get dizzy.

Trees mark our history, mine and En's: the magnolias and the monkey puzzle outside the hospital where we worked and met.

155

History marked into the trees En planted, a tree for the baby we lost and how the soil resisted. It was his mother's birthday, her seventieth. Everyone gathered. En and I snuck off to the field – there's an expression – off to the field his father had left him, years back, where we planted the tree for our child that wasn't, a May, the season and the name – the tree's, not the child's. How well it's done, that tree. In the centre is the conker tree he planted for Luke, the beech for Hugo. Sweet chestnut for D, the London plane for me that died; the eucalyptus that fell over in his absence. That one was in our back garden. I practice the name of each tree as he taught me over time, to recognise oak, Scots pine, yew, elm, wild cherry, dogwood, weeping ash; all those trees planted for the hell of it, for the love of it. It was the naming of trees that marked each car ride, each walk, each holiday. Each meeting and parting took place under trees.

We walked less when your letter first arrived. We talked less about trees, momentarily forgot trees. Finding them again in a temporary shelter we call home. Here in Spain. Hidden away on a hillside, on a pinprick stuck in a map.

~

Perec is smiling at me. A book of his that arrived just before we left home for this trip, the book with Perec's face on the cover, his *Species of Spaces*. His smiling face looking through a tall window, a window that reaches to the floor, a call back to the abandoned book. We write about home inspired by Perec's book that opens from a single blank page, via a room, rooms that open the home like a doll's house, along the street, the neighbourhood, ending with the universe. Like when you were a child and wrote your name in the front of every book ending in, The World, Space… The space and place of home. Perec's book I dog-ear, carry everywhere. We write about place and home, and belonging or not, bedrooms, hotel rooms, unusual conditions – a night train we take. Someone said to me that maybe this book, this letter to you, is a book that is really all about home. A home we took for granted, a home that gives the impression of safety, double glazing, front gates, hedges, walls, industrial brick…

Granted there's a wall, Perec wrote, *what's going on inside it…*

Before we came here, I dragged En to the museum one Sunday. Wanting to share with him a short video I'd watched only days earlier, a small video of a group of Afghan men in flowing clothes, pulling on lengths of white ropes; pulling En into the dark space of the gallery, into the blackness where at first we couldn't find our way, walking blindly toward the flickering of the film, Lida Abdul's *What I Saw Upon Awakening.* Fifteen or more Afghan men pulling on long white ropes, ropes some had wound around their waists or arms to give them more leverage. The camera panning out to expose the yards of ropes stretching into the distance attached to the shell of a bombed-out house. The dry earth where men slip on small yellow rocks as they pull and tug at what's left of a home that won't be moved. That home that is no more, tugged by yards and yards of rope wound around the men, wound around the walls that will not fall. En complaining that they are not pulling hard enough. – It's too set up, he said. Obviously they'll never pull that down, nor are they meant to.

I wanted to defend the men, the home, but from what? I wanted the house to move, to fall, to stay put. What's left of it; defiant like the small boys in the next room, next film, tottering on bricks: *The Brick Sellers of Kabul.* The seduction of early morning or evening light, if not dust everywhere obscuring the sun to an orange haze; the boys wobble on the bricks they are about to sell. They queue patiently, one by one bricks are exchanged for banknotes that flutter in the wind and may at

157

any time blow away, unlike the bricks that are collected by the man and piled into a solid cube. A man buying bricks children have gathered from a war-torn land, each brick bought and stacked, paper notes fluttering in the breeze, in the hands of the seller, between his hands and the children's – money-bricks. How much is a brick worth, a brick to throw or build with?

I never thought about the vulnerability of doors and windows and flimsy panelling until your letter came. I remember that our builder, trying to knock down a small section of our kitchen, kept telling me how strong our house was, built post-war, a new home built on a bombed-out house, during the war, two streets flattened, rebuilt, the builder said, from impenetrable bricks, engineering bricks. Nothing's as strong these days, he said. They don't make bricks like this any more.

I'll huff and I'll puff…

Recalling that I always had more empathy for the pig with the straw, believing that the pig with the bricks was too arrogant, too full of his own self-knowing and importance. I wanted the straw to stand strong.

Here on the Spanish landscape, how solid these turned wheels of straw can look, littering the fields, lit up, pale gold; huge circles of straw we all want to touch. We stop the car for D one day so he can do just that. Watch him stride across the field. The cows are miniature in the distance. Watch me follow. Touch the strength of the rolled-up straw bigger than both of us. – It's like giant cereal waiting for milk. Yes, the wolf's breath should have failed each time, the challenge of brick that leads to the fate of chimney smoke; the pot, and singed hair of the *chinny-chin-chin*.

Do you not even have a proper house alarm, someone asked, one of those whoppers they screw to the outside wall, the lights, the fierce dog, never mind the rest… Before we left she'd said, – The lack of alarm is alarming.

~

From the gold room I can see that across the fields a house is being built, not far from what would have been the front of a now-ruined home abandoned to the garden. The house in ruins has broken walls, only a door that is barely held in place by the frame. Still, when local children play there, they play at entering and leaving the house by this single door. A child calls, knocks on the door – they can see their friend sitting in the earth where the living room once was. Still they knock on the door, still the child sitting inside pauses before answering. Makes their friend knock twice. Runs off before she answers.

Makes me think of that game we'd play as children, Postman's Knock. All those old men who'd chase us down the road, sticks in hand, running in their carpet slippers. The cats joining in, – You little buggers! Old men left huffing and puffing.

It seems that my childhood was littered with the broken-down houses of others. Overgrown gardens where we'd roam and invent worlds, ships, castles; manor houses made from a simple two-up, two-down, the old, hidden inside the dark. The games we'd invent in their shadows, the companionship of birds, the graves of dead pets. Children inhabit the world of ants while the house looms large and inviting. We forget the earth when we grow; we forget the ant, the dust, the imprints.

I grew up inside a man's name. Walter Street. Each of the other streets named after the builder's brothers, Albert and Arthur. To sleep and eat and dream inside a Christian name, inside a row of houses that resembled a train, our street, the street opposite, like two night carriages passing in opposite directions, no stated destinations.

The first prize I ever won was for a painting I did of our streets, a watercolour of those rows of houses. I was under ten.

There was a post van in the painting – and so in the street – a post van delivering letters … imagine, letters! Autumn! First competition and first prize, dragging mother to see the painting displayed in the town hall. Eager hands pulling her up the hill to see the painting on the wall. Now we live in a red brick house, also inside a man's name. The street named after a disciple. Names and numbers, which number will I end with. Beginning 71, 10, 48, and 17 on to 30, final numbers, almost forgetting the lost brief number of my first home, 55.

From the gold room, the house in the making and the house in disrepair greet me each morning, both numberless. The old house has a fireplace still banked up with sticks where the birds now nest. Ash long blown along the stairs that go nowhere, only a chimney pot stands proud, erect and intact waiting for some warmth to rise. There's something about the empty door spaces, holes for windows, no protection, the spine of the house visible, the core, the staircase going nowhere. The staircase some say is the safest part of the house. You'd find more people sheltering under the stairs in air raids than squeezed up the chimney. All those bombed-out homes where the staircase failed to break apart. A staircase that fills you with an impulse to explore, to take steps, to trespass, that causes you to ask what hiding places are left.

On our walks we invite ourselves into rubble, stare inside the nailed-up orifices we are forced to peer inside, all that is left of abandoned homes, the mill with the enormous wheel still intact. Some resemble a child's drawing. Asking En if he remembers that time, well before the children were born, when we'd come across a disused farm, the contents of the house intact as if people were just out for the day. The clock had stopped at eleven minutes to four. I remember time held there like that, things in the sink, provisions in the larder, birds nesting in the cupboard, dogs cocking up their legs, picking over the debris, disturbing the birds for a while. We carried old kettles home that day, remember … a few cans we'd planned to plant up with geraniums, but never did. How we'd later regretted all we'd taken, a theft of sorts even to enter the house at all. Inside we'd found chairs beside the hearth just as in my grandparents' house, their two red fireside chairs, forty years either side of the hearth facing each other.

No door no need for keys…

I had a boyfriend once who was an Asian Catholic. The Catholic part confused me. I wanted his religion to be more *abroad*, less European. He would keep his keys hooked beneath pictures on the wall. Nana Mouskouri and the Virgin Mary, who over time merged into one. I did not have the look or the personality of either; it seemed obvious that it was a relationship destined to fail, to last only for five years, five years in which I'd witness his rather endearing habit when preparing to leave the house of picking up his keys and each time kissing Our Lady – or maybe I should say his lady. He had this way of always kissing his lips to his fingers, which were then pressed to Our Lady's face. His lips never kissed hers directly, for the lips of the mother of God were not meant for such advances. – Let's go, he'd say to me. Go, so we can come back. Each time we left his home, his room with the pictures of Nana next to the Virgin – he'd kiss only the Virgin, never Nana – unless he'd sneak a kiss to her in my absence. – Let's leave so we can come back, he'd say. Go and come. We leave, we are already arriving, we depart and it's already all over, we are already headed in the opposite direction.

After your letter arrived I could not think about going out and coming back in the same way. Couldn't think of keys in the same way. Over time I remembered again my love of keys. Time stalks the weather and all of it moves on, seasons, gardens, colours, words, misfortunes come and go, whisper and disappear without you really noticing how things return to a time when there was always something so satisfying about arriving home. Preparing to find the right key, to hold the key ready in the door, the small, often fiddly turn. There's nothing as useless as a big bunch of keys that have no lock, no home to go to. There was also a time in our lives when we had no keys. Now a keyless life is unimaginable.

I remember when a friend's father died. J's mother would go out just for something to do. Go to the butcher's – not out of hunger, but just to pass time, buy chops, sausages, cuts of ham. She'd order tongue because it had been her husband's favourite. She'd fill her bags up with corn-fed chicken and offal pies. She had a thing with the butcher. Nothing like you think. It was not that. She was alone. Her husband had been fond of meat and the butcher made time for her. He encouraged her to stay, to sit a while. She had a special corner in the shop, his side of the counter, where he'd leave a small chair out for her. He even made her tea. While she sipped, he'd prepare the meat. She wasn't squeamish, how could she be, she lived now by watching him work the knife. He took care with the details. The way he'd trim the fat off the heart made her almost cry. He'd let her talk. She didn't really go to the butcher for meat – they both knew that, but had no need to say that grief gave meat a sour odour, a consistency that stuck to the palette. If she were truthful she never ate the meat she bought, she'd carry it home wrapped in waxed paper. She liked the attention the butcher took with the wrapping, wrapping it as carefully as you would a birthday gift.

She'd cook the meat, she'd use herbs and sauces and stock, she'd simmer and baste, roast and carve, stick in cloves and garlic; she made accompaniments, she made her dead husband's favourite recipes; she'd talk to him while she cooked, boiled, brazed, glazed, scored the rind – she even tried out new recipes among old favourites as if to surprise him, then she'd eat a few mouthfuls, chew, spit out most, then bin the lot. All this to try to tell you that when she lost her husband it was keys that began to frighten her most: clock keys, keys to the wardrobe, music box, chest, heart, door, side view. The slow walk home from the butcher, when in the past she would have taken more direct routes. Now she'd meander through the park, taking the long way round, the park where the wrapped meat lay next to her in her bag, the dogs drooling for her cuts – it amused her to tease them, it passed more time. Keys in her pocket stop her wanting to return, when once she'd happily carried the parcels home, anticipated him being there. Home time, to be greeted, to have him relieve the weight of plastic and string marking her fingers, to have him heap the spill of it all onto the table, the sound that made, things relaxing, rolling, a stray orange lost to the floor, the feel of his hands cupping hers, rubbing free the numbness while the kettle whistled, while she unwrapped each twist of brown paper, talking him through each purchase … *Look, I got …*

It was the keys that became a mark of her grief, the keys she had never really thought of until now, the keys she'd taken for granted all those forty years of him being there, her door, his door, exact keys copied, bunched up, colour-coded, kept on a piece of old string, attached to a tiny brass anchor, a faded photograph, in the pocket, trouser, outside leg, his, hers, button, zip, purse, coat, cardigan, depending on the weather; keys she no longer wanted to use because she no longer wanted to go inside, to hear the natter of the radio, to unwrap each item, to remember how she'd once held a peach to his nose. She didn't want to find herself just looking from the kitchen window to check, each time, if the shrubs he'd planted were still in bloom.

It is not a matter of opening or not opening the door, Perec says, *not a matter of leaving the key in the door. The problem isn't whether or not there are keys: if there wasn't a door, there wouldn't be keys.*

We frighten ourselves when we peep, and sometimes it's thrilling what the eye wants. The empty rooms and the dust caught in sun. Abandon our eye to the rituals and tastes of strangers. Women telling me that they used to leave their doors open once, years back, when they were children: we'd even go out for the day and leave the door open. No one ever worried. People would knock and enter without you even needing to move from your chair.

In my chair in the sun, one late afternoon on the balcony of the gold room, a belly full with lunch, the taste of salt on my lips, my son D below in the yard in his rocking chair, listening to his music, the rhythm of the chair and the gentle pulse causes me to doze, to dream of the sea. Of being underwater...

The sea was a beautiful clear pale mint. Already I had heard someone say – I can swim but I'm not keen on water. The sea was calm. I saw a door float over me on the surface of the sea. It was a blue door, like our door at home. Sky-blue, the door like a raft I swam after. Swimming higher to reach the surface, to reach the door that was floating by too rapidly, to catch the door, to ring the bell, to knock. Is a door technically a door without walls? Without a home, without cement, people inside; what use the bell, what use the door, what is a door without hinges, screws, bolts, chains, spy holes, glass, letterbox. I catch the door and cling to it. Knock, call out, *It's only me... Yoo-hoo...* The brass letterbox glints, flaps open and closed – open and closed, but there is no news. *No news is good* ... they say. The letterbox shines under the sea. The sun filters through the surface and through the letterbox. No mail today but the sun in my eye breaks open the spy-hole, elongates a fish into a monster. The violence of the bell fills the sea, causes the waves to rise; the demand of a bell, the silence between; the still-unanswered question of who will attend to this silence, this call. The door slips away and passes out of reach. Have I lost the door now, the dream door ... I was relying on it, swimming for it. I couldn't swim fast enough. Realising as I watched it go that I have forgotten the password Father taught us as children to let us in through the front door. All meant as a lark.

It's hard obviously to imagine a house which doesn't have a door... Perec wrote, *You can't let yourself slide from one to the other from the private to the public you have to have the password, have to cross the threshold, have to show your credentials, have to communicate, just as the prisoner communicates with the outside world.*

Telling En my dream, the dream of doors and suddenly doors are everywhere, the coincidence of doors; images of doors. – Remember the story of the man, En says, who built a house made up of many, many doors, both inside and out, more than your average number of doors. A man opening and closing the doors just for the pleasure. – Remember that time when we woke to the sound of the man in the river; we watched him through the window, he was standing waist-deep in water in the moonlight, his white shirt lit up, echoing cries of *door, door, door.*

Watch the men now from the window of the gold room. Men in the distance, men returning from their afternoon sleep to the other side of the abandoned house. Over time, a family, a community, different generations of skin, hands, limbs, join in, all curl in a line passing water for the cement, pails of water one way, pails of rubble the other. The cement mixer, remember those round open bellies turning the mix. As children we'd sit mesmerized by the change from wet grit to thick creamy cement. Those mixers that would later be emptied and cleaned, turning as the children climbed in, like Diogenes coming home to his barrel. There's a line of people in the distance passing each other pails of water for the cement. There are men with plumb lines and spirit levels. Another thing we'd fight over as children: the different-sized lime green bubbles held to the light, to every surface, even, uneven, my turn, your turn. What patience and care it takes to build a house. Always the holes left for looking through, for air and answering, calling, daydreaming, waiting for the post. Can you hear that: the sound of men nailing in the doorframe, four others silently carrying the door waist height, one at each corner, men already screwing in the locks.

D's reply to questions I put to him concerning the letter

I didn't receive the letter, Dad did.

I remember being in my room when you or both of you told me. I think it was you who told us.

I always think of Dad as real masculine; he's not one for smiling a lot or crying. I pictured Dad as less powerful when he got the letter, what's the word … something … well, he was more vulnerable.

I can't remember if I was worried or sad, or what I felt.

Are you writing things down, writing everything down that I say? Are you writing that down? That's reminding me of the woman at school who used to come and ask us questions, and if you were struggling to read a word she'd write things down, make notes about you struggling, or whatever it was she wrote down about us. We called her the red ball woman, cos she pronounced words in this exaggerated manner because we have dyslexia, Hugo and me; she thought we were somehow deaf as well. Thick and deaf, because she'd pronounce everything in this exaggerated way to Hugo and me, and she'd roll her *rrrrr*s and she'd say things like *the rrrrrred ball*. Like, *Susie has a rrrrrrred ball. What does Susie have?* And she'd write everything down you were saying without showing you, with her hand over the page and a real serious expression like she knew things about you that you didn't, or couldn't, know yourself.

When the letter came I think I was hungry. I think it was you who said, Gather round boys, sit down, I have something to tell you … or something like that. You told us that Dad had gotten a threatening letter from someone connected to work at The Quad and you had to explain and tell us because there would be times when we were alone in the house and we had to be careful about locking things up, keeping our phones on, and opening the door. I remember you were worried about leaving us alone, but we made you go out.

Someone had written the letter on a manual typewriter to make it look authentic. Or maybe that's what we said… It made it look like a letter you'd see in a film, written in World War Two or something.

I didn't read it. I just felt different toward Dad for a while, my perception of him, until we got back to arguing about the usual things like washing up and then it was just Dad being Dad again.

I'm not scared of no crazy typewriter fool. I was more worried that our mail was going to get wet, my music magazines and things, when those two women fitted the mailbox to the back of the door, and we had fire extinguishers inside that would put out any fire bombs or exploding things someone might post. I thought, is all this necessary? I liked the peephole because it made people at the door look as if their heads were elongated and huge. I was more worried that the postman thought we were crazy as often he couldn't get our mail through the hole like he used to, cos the new letterbox inside was blocking its fall and it makes a noise of metal, all hollow and tinny, it isn't like a sound or anything anyone else in the street has.

I'm not one to think about threats and things like that. I keep it real. I think about things but then say to myself, what's the worst that could happen, some guy breaks Dad's legs, gets him in the street, but I didn't think of the worst thing. I thought it, and then thought it wouldn't happen. Daydreaming; imagine. I think Dad's tough anyway – physically, not so much mentally tough – well not that he isn't, but have you ever had an arm wrestle with him? He's got more than enough strength to punch someone, defend himself, but what I mean is, mentally he is not the kind of person to think to defend himself.

Can we move on to talking about Spain yet, and the bullfight? Now they did get stabbed, those bulls we saw at the end of our holiday? – and there you are worrying about Dad. I don't think you've written about the bullfight yet, not properly typed it up yet –

Anyway. I've got a good imagination but a lot of common sense.

Yes, I felt sorry for Dad that he'd got the letter, but that's all I felt. I wasn't worried, but I was for the bull. I feel for the bull but not in a way some do, people who really protest about it, chain themselves to the gates of the *corrida*, vegetarians. They think we don't feel sorry for the bull but we do. I wanted him to get stabbed but at the same time I didn't. The bull, yes, I wanted both things. The men on the horses, the picadors, scared me most of all; the horses shouldn't get into the mess they are forced into, somehow, they should learn to say No. I felt scared for the matador, for the man. I wrote that I was scared for the bull when I wrote the story afterwards, for school, for my course work, *imaginative writing*. I wrote I was scared for the bull just to get extra marks. I felt more scared for the man. Both are true.

When Dad got the letter I think I felt as safe and as bored as I usually do.

Hugo's reply to questions I put to him concerning the letter

I never saw the letter. I didn't read it. I think you said you
didn't want us to because it wasn't something we should see.
What sort of interviewing technique is this anyway… If this
was *Desert Island Discs* with Sue … no, Kirsty … they don't
just say, Tell me about … and move quickly on to some music.

It was a Tuesday and a particularly windy day when the
letter arrived. Raining but not enough to get wet.

Dad got a baseball bat down from the chimney – no, the loft,
he was saving it for a rainy day, no pun intended. He kept it by
the door and I liked playing about with it when you weren't in
and telling me not to.

You were going through a phase of eating fennel at the time;
we were not.

I had English the following day at school. I thought I'd
write a story about it, the letter, but that if I did write it, no
one would believe me.

It wasn't really directed at me so I didn't feel anything much,
it's just talk.

A bit unusual, that he had a typewriter, whoever wrote it,
like he's watched too many movies, or had the technology of
a caveman.

Guess what … about the letter … as I was saying…What
was I saying?… You are writing things down that I'm saying
aren't you?

I felt hungry when the letter arrived.

I don't believe you that D said the same thing.

God, you're weird; I've been threatened so many times in
school before. The letter didn't change anything. Except isn't it
worse if you don't know who the people are who are threatening
you? If someone you know throws a piece of paper at you with
your name on then what does that do, does it bother you?

Depends on the circumstances. But you can only go so far with a piece of paper can't you? ... Well, the letter was on a piece of paper so you obviously can go far.

The alarm under the TV looked like a Nintendo and I wanted to press the big red button to see what would happen, to see if the police would really come – even though people were telling me not to push the button I really wanted to. Well, you told me to push it if something happened if you were out, but I don't know if I would have, even though I wanted to.

I quite liked the letterbox. It almost spoke to me. We had conversations about how he'd read the mail when he found mail in his mouth, except the bills and bank statements bored him. It was and is a very surreal letterbox. I've forgotten what the letterbox used to be like before. I've got used to it all but when they put the junk mail and newspapers in they'd stick out because things now got stuck in the mouth and so on my way to school I would think, I hope no one's noticed them sticking out, because nobody else's was sticking out, so it made our house stick out, and I wondered what the postman thought and if he knew that we've got this nonsensical mailbox-come-fire extinguisher.

Sometimes in Tesco or whatever shop we were in, I would worry that some man would come and pretend he was someone else and come and get Dad while asking him where the pasta is but instead of picking up the tagliatelle he'd get him.

Maybe I've been lying through the whole interview – it shows how powerful the interview process is, it just shows what power you can have over an interviewer, you ask me questions and write down whatever I say, but you never know if what I say is what I mean to say. I could say that this is part one and now part two I'll get more emotional and tell you how it really is, how I really felt, or I may say, this is now the end of the interview and I am not giving you part two, instead I am going out. Yes, I could say at any moment: I finish now; I'm off out now to Chicken Plus with my friend, so I won't be able to resume this interview for some time, if at all. It may never be possible to ascertain ... what does ascertain mean? ... what I thought of the letter. What it was like for D and me, except to say that the letter made us both hungry. We didn't know this as we hadn't shared this with one another – our hunger, and we only shared this with you during separate interviews, privately. We still wouldn't know – except you told me – D said that too, that when the letter came he was hungry and come to think of it, this interview is also making me hungry – so much so, I am now planning to go to Chicken Plus. This is not the response you expected, but maybe that's as good as it gets...

Day Pages – Spain

In the house in Spain there is no post – well, not for us; no one knows where we are, no more than the rough location, there's only me sending letters and cards all around the world. I have learned to liberate myself from the restraint of onionskin for those abroad and write on whatever comes to hand. It's only me searching out the post offices of various cities. Can you really know your way around a city until you have located the post office? – the vaulted ceilings, the pillars, marble floors and steps, carvings, not that dissimilar from the museums. Join the shuffle of quiet queues, wait your turn for the damp orange sponge, the repetitive background thump of the rubber hitting the inkpad, hitting the envelopes again, again, six in a row, unless you use the *estancos* here, the small unassuming stores. The estancos that sell tobacco, top-shelf magazines, toys, sweets, stamps in huge ledgers. I have in many ways lost the art of letter-writing, like most people, now so used to the cut-and-paste, to a different speed. This letter to you is an inadequate response, to open my notebook and find that the words needed are not there. To think too much about words, words I mostly get wrong.

Today at the post office here in Spain inside a type of annex, dark relief from the sun, and at the foot of the rather grand marble staircase, unexpected pleasures, the coolness of the staircase and beneath it, the two twenty-foot costumes, headless beings, arms outstretched to greet us. One large red satin jacket, almost a clown's coat, one gold brocade suit, as gold as my temporary room. Broad shoulders, exaggerated unless you happened to be a giant – the giant we all longed for from our mother's bed, way back, when she read the story of *Jack and the Beanstalk*. So much wanted from a bean, from a sold worn-down cow. – What's a cow without udders, Luke said, – Write it down! What's a costume this size without the giants to fill them, the promise of their existence somewhere, the possibility of a couple, siblings, lovers, twins, spare cloth, messy pup; maybe unborn, these giants still to grow, maybe waiting in the postmistress's belly. The five red buttons of their coats I cannot reach, try as I might. Forgive my enthusiasm. I descend the stairs again before we even reach the first floor; someone on their descent telling us that the post office is shut. Shut for an hour. They do that here. The post office worker is missing with the giants. Run amok. The costumes we again admire; what else is there to do but to repeat the moment, take our time, feel the fabric, the silk … look at us all grinning up at these empty suits, not a face between them, our faces barely crotch-height, forgetting the letters in our hands – delayed – unposted, later binned.

~

We had a dog when I was a child; we had many dogs. They came along one at a time. Most were mad. Most we had eventually to give away. My dad would bring them home for birthdays, Christmases, after the pub closed, someone selling potatoes and puppies off the back of a lorry. A house is safe when you have a dog, they say. Some say, a dog's not just for Christmas. A cat sees to itself. A cat does not know how to defend a house from intruders. Some even postpone the dog and buy a device that instead activates an electronic bark – woof-woof – extra howls switched on with any sign of a stranger coming along the path. Boxing was and is my father's favourite sport and boxers his favourite dogs. Although we had an array of cross-breeds, mongrels some would say, most were boxers. My mother went into hospital around the time that the first boxer appeared. A teacher asked me each day if we were being cared for well, and if so, was our father managing. – Yes sir …

Proud enough, almost a scene from Dickens … – I am happy, sir. Please sir, he sends me on small errands, messages, at odd times of the day. We eat. – What? he asked. Perking up: – Sir, we eat Fray Bentos beef pies, sir; each lunchtime, the ones you get in tins. The puff pastry is always golden and rises so high and you wouldn't believe the volume, its transparency and the delicate leaves. When he places it on the table we sigh. Sir, I swear it's like putting your knife into an angel's back. For afters we eat dark toffee apples. My mother cut open somewhere in the distance could not afford such decadence at school lunchtimes. This is how it goes …

Mother would write me letters from her hospital bed. These were the first letters I ever gave or received. It began my attachment to, my longing to give and receive letters. It began my twenty-pagers, my love of writing, exaggeration, digression, without realising I was wandering or making things up. I had a pen-pal later. She lived in Newcastle and had an odd accent even when writing. We both had pets called Sam: mine a guinea pig, hers a pet beetle. We never met. Mother, in her letters, told me things she'd never told me before – but nothing sensational. The tiny details, banalities at the heart of all letters, small affections, memories, humour we share; maybe of no interest to anyone else, but what I came to love about them was the sound of her voice up close, just for me. Obliged to re-read them, wanted to, until I knew them by heart; Father re-reading my letters to Mother when he visited her. I even drew a stamp on the envelopes and could do good likenesses of the Queen at different angles. We were only a ten-minute walk away, ten short minutes from where he carried the letters to the place she lay; when he carried the letters he walked out of the house, up the set of steps opposite, around the top lane, across the top terrace, up the second bigger hill and there was the hospital – the hospital that used to be the workhouse, and the hospital where I was born. Imagine, the words carried from me to Mother, and from her back to me, on thin airmail paper – all Father could find, even though he walked not flew, our letters' transparency almost as edible and light as his tinned puff pastry. Those letters where she'd laugh at the way I misspelled *hopital*. Laughed or maybe cried, holding down her belly where it hurt, when I'd write that our boxer dog ate my slippers, my mules. Why they are called after a donkey, I never knew. I woke to the dog's chops covered in pale blue feathers, small silk rose buds stuck in his teeth. I told Mother that one lunchtime the dog ate my box of ten jumbo crayons. – He's been shitting rainbows all week, all over the lawn, came out in large lumps over his gold coat. I think at the time I said poo, not shit. I told her that the dog whimpered and Father said he'd get over it, the dog would move on soon to colouring his tail where he licks. The dog had been trying to make a puppy with the bitch across the road, but mother didn't need to know that either, not yet. Father said her stitches would ache if she knew all that went on in her absence. I kept the letters nice, the ones I sent. The ones I received. Tied them in a bow the way people do. With a small ribbon, what was left of my chewed-up mules.

Miriam's story

It started with a phone call to say that someone had been referred to me for counselling, as I do see people privately, and I said yes. Following on from that came the phone call from the person herself. When she rang she wanted to unravel her story on the phone right there, and I had to say that it wasn't appropriate to go into it then. I agreed to meet her for one session to see if we were compatible and able to work together. She came to my home, as at that time the place I usually use as an office was unavailable because I had someone living in it. And so I had to conduct this one-hour session in my living room, which was in the flat behind the shop where I have a small gallery. And even though I embarked on that and tidied away personal effects of mine, which you are supposed to do in a counselling situation – make the surroundings bland and uninformative about your own personal disposition – even though I did that, I knew that having her in my home was the wrong thing to do, even though I know lots of people who do counsel from their homes. Looking back, one thing that now comes to mind and later bothered me was that she had a burning desire to use the bathroom all the time, and did several times during the one-hour sessions – sessions where she explained her story and her experiences. I saw this person for quite a long time, maybe eighteen months in total, but during the period of seeing her, she managed to get some information about my private life at a barbecue she'd been at, and suddenly was aware, or so she thought, of my sexual orientation, in which she delighted.

From what she'd said, there were other people she'd fixated on, people who had been in counselling or caring roles with her, but the fact that she had this bit of gossip on me, that I'd once lived with a woman … She thought that the green light was on, and that it was a foregone conclusion that we were going to have some kind of relationship. I dealt with it by not revealing anything about my personal life. She wanted the information to be confirmed and spent lots of time trying to do that with anyone she could find to ask.

The counselling got very difficult because she started coming late for sessions or wanted to run over. Then she started sending me cards with rabbits on, or cute kittens; letters too. Some of them would say I was the best thing that ever happened to her. A week later I'd get another letter saying the complete opposite, with quite explicit language. She also would accuse me of being a bad practitioner, would say that she needed counselling to get over the counselling, that I was devious, that I wasn't telling the truth – not that I had anything to tell. Just seeing my name on the letters, or the cheap envelopes she'd use or the smiley faces and the little drawings she'd put onto the envelopes was enough to let me know as soon as the letter arrived that it was her again.

The first time I started to get really scared was the day she sat on the wall outside my gallery – the gallery has a very large window – and stared in at me for about an hour. Then she went from there to a café opposite and got a chair on the pavement and stared across for about another hour. When she'd finished she came into the gallery as if she were a customer. I sometimes worked on my own in the gallery and she knew that. She said she needed to know if the information she thought she had about my sexual orientation was true. And I had to keep saying, it's not in any way relevant. By then, she was after a relationship of equality. Friends together around the table, having a coffee, maybe more. And even though I tried every trick I'd been taught to keep things between us professional – that's worked with all the other people I've seen over the last nearly fifteen years of counselling – it didn't work with this woman. I began to reflect on the fact that she'd been in my home, seen my things, used my bathroom and sat on my lavatory seat. That now felt such an invasion. She'd seen my tortoises outside and that also felt an intrusion. She even started talking about my tortoises in the cards she sent. Something as stupid as that became ... well, I even began to feel that they were vulnerable, they are portable, and I began to get quietly terrified really.

Then the letters came at least once a week. An example being one Sunday afternoon when I was sitting in my flat. The front door of the flat opens directly onto the pavement – no porch, no hallway or anything, and I was just sitting there minding my own business and this chubby hand started wiggling through the letterbox and dropped yet another card, so I knew that she was out there. She didn't ring or knock – she just lingered with her fingers. She knew I was in; my car was there she could hear my music.

When you get letters from someone who is in this frame of mind, just their handwriting, just the shape of the initial of your name is like ... I mean rape is too strong a word, but that's the flavour, of something touching you in a way you don't want to be touched.

What it also did was challenge my professionalism, challenge my integrity. These things challenge who you are, what you do, what you've said. I started to wish that I'd taped and video-recorded every session I'd ever had with her, because I kept seeing myself in a court of law and someone saying, ah but ... you touched her shoulder as she left your house. You can read all the books in the world that tell you what you should and shouldn't do and say, but at the end of the day it's just two human beings in a room, and there's not a counsellor in the land or maybe a driving instructor or teacher who doesn't sometimes worry about being accused of something. The intimacy of the situation can too easily be misread.

I was speaking to someone the other day who said some kids had got on to the roof of a church and were smashing it up,

179

and the Catholic priest came out saying, – You little blighters, get off the roof of the church. To which they said, – We'll go to the police and tell them that you asked us to give you a blow-job. He had to go back into the presbytery and let them carry on because he didn't dare go any further. That is an extreme example – but when he told me that, I thought, well, that's in some ways the position I found myself in.

I know I keep on about the toilet seat but it was huge in my … I changed it actually, I changed the toilet seat, it became the interface between her and me, between her telling me that she was in love with me, that she wanted to travel the world with me. The other thing that would happen was that she would ring my place of work and my colleague would give her all sorts of bits of information inadvertently. She found out that my daughter had just given birth. She found out that she lived in Scotland. She'd write and say she could fly up to Scotland with me as my travelling companion to see my new grandchild. She'd said she could stay in a hotel – that I could go and see the baby and then return to be with her.

Usually when I opened the letters I'd show them to friends or colleagues straight away because I wanted someone else to see, to not have this to myself. And their response was always, get a solicitor, go to the police, don't put up with this. There was a need to share, but that reinforced my feeling, you're supposed to be professional, you're supposed to be … well, confidential, but by that time the letters were coming thick and fast and I had terminated the counselling. We'd even had a session to end the sessions. I gave her other information on other counselling groups or people she might get in touch with.

When I stopped seeing her I was told to write a formal letter saying stay away; any more contact of any kind and there'll be a court order against you. I don't know why but I couldn't do it. I did write a very formal letter to her and typed it. It didn't work because she immediately wrote back ignoring the content and saying that she really liked my handwriting and why did I need to type a letter to her.

I think knowing who is writing the letters to you is different to not knowing. It's not about it being better or worse. Maybe it's like having mice or rats or something and it's worse finding the droppings and not being sure whether you've got them or not, but then when you see a mouse run across your floor it's horrid but at least you know, at least you can do something about it.

Having said that, I know the face of this person very well and I have looked at it for, what, some twenty hours – maybe more – but then I don't know her at all. I often thought maybe she was capable of anything.

My brother came to visit me once, he's a bit of a joker, and I told him about it. I suddenly wanted to feel protected from her and I told him and all he could say was, – It's not very good where you live, you could be coming home late one night and she could jump out with a knife. And that terrified me. He didn't realise what he'd done because after he'd said this, and when the letters kept coming, I realised that I had to move house. I moved house not completely because of her but because the whole experience caused me to think about my safety and I think in part the move was a need to want to be anonymous again.

I feel safe in this new house but I don't really like it – I'm trying to like it but I much preferred where I lived before. In order to move I had to borrow hundreds of thousands of pounds; when I did move the power of her letters and threats then hit me.

I don't keep her letters to hand. I don't look at them any more but I'd hate to not have them because they are proof – most of the letters and cards I ripped up straight away.

I think you just get to a time when you don't want to talk about it any more. I haven't thought about what happened for a long time now but what was strange today was my ability to put my hands on the letters in an instant. I don't know anything else I could put my hand on that quickly; normally it would take me ages to find anything – my filing cabinet is full of things in the wrong order – but I found the letters immediately. I also didn't realise how many I'd kept.

Today I allowed myself, in words at least, to follow a woman from the café.

All this prompted by a friend, Louisa, telling me of a woman she knew who wrote everything down on till receipts, pinned them to the wall. The same woman would stalk people in supermarkets. Would follow people and their trolleys. She'd follow them home – on the bus, by foot, for whatever part of the day she could keep it up. She knew it was wrong but continued anyway. She'd tell Louisa that it didn't matter if it was a man or a woman, but that it had something to do with the things they'd put in their trolley, the choices they made that grabbed her attention. In the same way, you could say, that the woman in the café grabbed mine…

A woman in the café is gathering her things and getting ready to leave. I don't ponder on the gender but I admit that to follow a man may have felt more of a challenge. I watch her sip the last of her Earl Grey, gather the final objects she scattered around her, back into her bag, now zipped, wave to the café owner, reapply outdoor clothes, silk scarf tucked in, my body working ahead of me, closing my notebook or maybe not, to close or not close, to write to imagine or to follow her closely as she closes the door.

I'll let you decide whether I get up as she closes the door; whether, as she closes the door, I open it again, so soon. She is ahead of me now; how else can we follow. She looks decisive enough. I wonder if she is going to meet someone. I hadn't really studied her any more or less than anyone else in the café; it was less of a choice, and more that I had been sitting in the café that morning writing about the potential to act on what would normally be no more than a twitch in the knee, a tap of the foot. More that with your letter came the constant notion that you were behind us, like in the pantos – that call, that flinch, to turn the head this way and that. As we walked and drove and shopped and moved in and out of the garden, yes, since you wrote, the instinct to turn became exaggerated and not a principal boy or dame in sight. Or wasn't it more that when she got ready to leave and was up on her feet, at that moment I simply found myself also moving to follow...

Yes, the woman looks decisive enough from the way she walks straight and proud, a little canter to her step. As she waves to someone ahead, my body tightens, so soon pulling back, sure I've been discovered with only yards covered, sure I'll need to halt all steps between us, abort, if she embraces this other, leaving me with nowhere to go but on or back, to side-step into a shop for hearing aids – something I have no need of yet. But no; after some time her ease of direction makes me realise that her wave is no more than a healthy greeting, a passing gesture, and that we are soon to be going home. That simple: already homeward bound – hers, not mine; she is not behind me, following. I have at present no pull toward my own home. I wonder if at some point she'll take the bus ... then what? Do I want to embark on that, a different kind of motion, where I'd maybe find myself forced to sit beside her, or to be that close to the back of her head, to see the hairs of her head part as she turns back and forth at the window.

Normally when I sit on the bus, old men, sometimes incontinent, more dribbles than a flood, sit next to me. It happens all the time these days; they sit next to me, or close enough that each inhalation fills me with a rush of ammonia. On the bus, as in the café, if I don't keep my body turned enough to the window; even a rigidity to the torso does little to stop the persistent among them telling me their life stories: their children's stories, their grandchildren, their dog died, the rent's due, share prices, cloudy expected rain, the price of pork loin – the men, watery eyes, corneas and bladders not what they

184

used to be. I feel I've wronged her in some way, the woman I am following, by thinking about incontinence while I keep myself as close by as I can, trying not to get too out of breath. I am sure she has no problem with continence. I can almost smell the lavender on her, the sweet pollen and the wash cubes, a little baby powder. She could be a mother, the way I'm following her – some kickback to earlier times, like those lambs who lose their mothers left wandering the roads, left to sidle up to the underbelly of any old ewe. Not that she was any old ewe. Something in her bold jewellery, in the way she wears a hat when she doesn't yet need to, encourages me on. This is how I am, seduced by a hat, a beret, its angle, dashing, gratifying, the colour grey that matches her coat, or rather, compliments it, her choice of blue grey boots; she holds herself upright in a way that almost tires me. I imagine that she has large nostrils, and while preparing to laugh or begin a long sentence she could inhale me in a bout of curiosity, take me into her head.

It is then she turns. I have, as usual, allowed myself to daydream too much, to wander off. When she turns sharply my heart shifts in a way I have forgotten and I think I smile – more of a grimace, I show too many teeth then take them back, pretend I am squinting at the sky where I quickly hold my hand to my eyes as if I am looking for something that has floated from my gaze or grasp. It is not windy and she doesn't seem to notice or question. I want her to recognise me, or to tell me to shoo, to stop all this nonsense, be gone, shoo, shoo. To tell me that I was too close, am close enough now to see the stitching on her hem has come a little undone. The way the belt on her coat has missed a loop and is twisted. The way the heels of her boots have been repaired. When she turns she is not looking at me but beyond me, she is checking the traffic, or maybe she has forgotten something. I cannot be sure if she briefly eyes me, but we all do this so many times a day with no repercussions and no memory of who we see. Seconds pass. The eye cleans itself regularly with a meagre blink. We walk on a little more and I find my legs trembling but I keep them in motion, stiff, awkward steps, and we cross the zebra easily enough. I know I've made the right choice – the one that hadn't seemed a choice. As she takes a right turn, I can tell by her change in rhythm and the resonance of her walk that from here on it is – as they say – all downhill. I think of all the people who are out there today following others, first-timers like me, or artists well-versed, all part of the job, detectives, jealous husbands, dogs, people with dementia, lost children, all those potentials behind me – you behind En – all those snaking lines we potentially form one behind each other every day. Before the letter, how seldom we ever bothered to look behind us – who even checks the back of their hair, except every six weeks when the hairdresser holds you in those all angled floor-to-ceiling mirrors, always finishing with the hand-held, so proud of her work.

Finally it is just a short walk home, no more than five minutes. In some ways I expected more: more risk, more danger, that it would take more time, more turns, twists and obstacles. In the end it was easier than I imagined – not that I had imagined anything at all until Louisa put the thought into my head, asking, – Have you ever followed anyone, a stranger, anyone? Yes, you!

Finally, as I follow, I begin to imagine that we are already at her house, that she knows that I'll recognise the bulbs, the ones she'd planted in the disused toilet pan just beside the door. She has humour; I knew this by the way she angled her hat. I imagine that the first thing we'll do together will be to take out a newspaper, to put on the kettle. The kettle will be blue. I'll tell her mine is red. Hers, eggshell blue and a little chipped. It will have the sweetest of whistles, which she'll mimic while we spread the newspaper out on the floor of the living room.

I haven't taken to the floor like that since I was a teenager, since I drew, and later forgot that way with form and line and shadow. There we'll be on the floor, she and I, sipping tea again, having only just left the café – no more than a thing people do when they get home, even if they get home from a jaunt and a beverage; it's a habit of humans to drink more tea than they need. Here at least, here where she has a collection of tea caddies, most full, loose-leaf tea, clearly labelled, she keeps a tidy house. She has all the equipment: strainers, cosies – all one could require for a fresh brew. There we'll be on the rug, and we'll look up our horoscopes in the newspaper, and we'll see that we are possibly compatible but we'd not believe all that anyway, earth and water, dependable and tenacious, tactile and intuitive; and we'll read each other's lucky numbers, colour, birthstone, predictions that give no indication of our meeting, my straying far beyond the decorum that we normally keep in place with strangers we walk by, see across a room, someone that holds a door open for us, no more than the seconds we have.

It is then that I hear the key in the door and she snaps me out of whatever imaginative leaps I'd been making ahead of us as we walked the last lap home. Come in, she might have said, but knowing it often doesn't end this way. What the hell – we'll not be suspicious; instead we smile a little awkwardly, she more puzzled at my presence at her gate; she pauses to pull a few dead leaves from the flowers that stretch across the door, we briefly admire them in silence, the flowers and the colour as she wipes her feet on the doormat, more from habit than necessity, with only a brief nod before closing her door on me.

Day Pages – Spain

7am in the gold room. I open the shutters; the repetition of what has stayed the same, what has not changed in the view becomes a comfort. The sunflowers in the neighbouring field, so tall. Since last night their heads have been covered in plastic bags; they look as if they are lined up to die by firing squad. Bowed heads bound in different coloured plastic, reminding me of images of Abu Ghraib.

We listen to the sound of the digger in the fields. – One day, En says, I'm going to buy a digger and become a digger and I'll dig and other people will pay for me to dig with my digger and you can come and look at what I've dug each day and then no doubt there'll be some who will be jealous of my digging – the simplicity and the commitment of it, and I'll dig ditches in expanses of land, furrow the landscape, and I'll be happy to just dig.

Yesterday we visited a chorizo factory that we pass almost every day. I wanted to see how they made the meat sausages, how the process was carried out. I have to admit I'd expected live or whole pigs. When in fact there wasn't a pig anywhere to be seen. No smell. Not a grunt.

Fábrica de Chorizo, Mariano Olmas e Hijos S.L., Bernuy de Porreros.

Recipe:

Carne de cerdo
Sal
Pimentón dulce o picante
Orégano
Ajo

To make chorizo, the pig from the abattoir is gutted. Remove the shoulders and hind legs to make the hams, *lomo*, loin; all small pieces left over go through a coarse mincing machine. Hams are salted and hung in curing cupboards for six months; sausages are made by squeezing the mince into intestines, cows or pigs. Hang them for 4 to 5 weeks. The *cochinillas* are pigs slaughtered when they are just six months old. In winter they sell more sausages and pork products.

What to write about a chorizo factory we pass each morning, the red brick reminding me of the old psychiatric hospitals I'd worked in. Not forgetting the story of Adam the boar. Paid for out of En's mother's reparation from the Austrian government – Elise, who was forced to flee Vienna to escape the Nazi holocaust. She was eighteen. Adam the white boar was ageless. – Have you seen the size of a boar's penis, En says, measuring out a section of table in the factory to shock me a little. Hugo, interrupting, holding his hands wider. – Only a boar's ends in something like a corkscrew, En says, but with the thickness of a pencil. It often bends as the boar gets excited, so you have to guide it into the sow. Pigs gestate in three months, three weeks and three days. – Nah … you're making it up, Dad! – No I'm not! We'd rent out Adam to the local farmers who couldn't afford a boar. I don't remember what happened to Adam. Adam couldn't move with us … No, wait – maybe he came with us in a cattle truck. – Baboons squash their things into the ground, Hugo says, remember … the zoo we went to the other day and they were rolling out their willies on the ground as if they were making pastry for a pie.

In the chorizo factory, En explains to the owner that I am writing a book. He does not go into the details – not of the letter, not of you. The man asks if I am P.D. James and we all laugh. He says I must be writing a detective or a murder novel. – I hope not, I say, but he cannot see the joke in the same way we do.

The man hosing down the hams doesn't laugh. The man rolling the hams into salt doesn't laugh. In the cupboard into which we all squash, the cupboard where the hams are hung, we all stand and take photographs, we in our issued white coats, mine pristine and too big, Hugo's and Luke's smeared with blood like the blood on the floor, on the knives, a huge metal trolley on wheels covered in entrails and blood and mince. D has refused to come in and waits in the car. He says we are all mad to want to look at a factory of dead pigs, even though – where are the pigs? Only their parts hang, racks of chorizo like necklaces, everything at different stages of drying. At the entrance to the factory – which is actually quite small once we're inside – more chorizo are displayed in the tiny shop. We buy some and the man wraps it carefully in waxed paper. Gives us plenty to try. There's a photograph on a table of an enormous black pig lying across the ground, blubber everywhere, his proud white snout finding the air. The pig is wearing a rosette, and beside the photograph a ceramic piggy bank.

~

I'm noticing that since Luke began writing each morning, reading to me each evening, every conversation, observation, is in danger of becoming a song lyric. Earlier this morning, En had stopped the car and the conversation abruptly to check if there was any water in the river beneath the small bridge we drove over. – Without water, Luke says, is a river technically a river? That's a lyric in the making, he laughs: a line in the off-hours. The calmative effect of sharing our stories, the way he lures strangers to him, unknowing how or why it is that when we are out walking, or when he is just sitting somewhere, head down, or gazing into some distance, they find their way to him. Stories ready to tell. Yes, these past days, I'm noticing that

190

when we are out, same patterns, all innocent enough, strangers approach, old men ask him his name. Bent over him with their walking sticks in their hands, cardigans stretched, trouser arse sagging, same grey cloth. I watch them, speculate about what they say to him, try to translate, watch from a short distance, trying not to intrude. Usually he is wandering off to have a cigarette when they approach. The way they smile at him, the way he returns what they've lost. What was that? – They've lost their way to tomorrow – another lyric, Luke says. Write it down. Laugh about it. Old men with no concerns about what he can or cannot understand of their Spanish, all gums and whiskers. That won't do. The youth they see in him, the way his arm flexes when he holds a cigarette – they smell it, young flesh and smoke. They search him out. – I can talk to them, he tells me. That way he has, that way he knows, even in pidgin English, I believe him. I see it. Here I am, over here watching. Soon enough we'll be cardiganed, our pants and arses sagging, our sticks warm in our hands, soon we'll chasing after strangers trying to tell them what cannot really be told.

~

What happens to all the tall skinny women here? Do they turn into the short square grannies who come to walk the quiet tracks we take to each evening? The grannies out walking pass us in the road … Each morning, each evening, we walk together. Various combinations, rarely all. Tonight it's D, En and me, and the grandmothers who pass us, six of them in a line. – *Pasa,* they say, acknowledging that we should be faster than them. Tonight we are racing, walking as fast as we can to catch up, as we watch the line of six already well ahead of us as we reach a brow of the hill, the sun ahead. The group of six is silhouetted, their shadows, their shapes defined. They are wearing their best clothes, in the middle of these fields and hills and stone paths, they carry shiny handbags and umbrellas to keep off the sun. Folded for now on their arms. The grannies wear lipstick – that restores my faith – and powder and tiny earrings that flash in the evening light. What will happen when the other set of grandmothers – also six in number – moving west to east – meet the line of six moving from east to west? They are hazy in the sun. It's like watching an army advance on both sides. In that old-fashioned way, when armies would advance toward each other in battle. It could go either way. They could fight with rolled umbrellas and handbags. They could embrace and dance. They could swap partners, change the order of both collections of women, all possible combinations. For a moment it's like a chess game in which a hand is pushing all the pieces: even the Queens move on each side. Carry the longest umbrellas and have the largest arthritic hips. We stand a while, place bets on what will happen in a minute when one group of six meets the other. We are nervous and excited by the possible outcomes. And finally, for sure, there is a knowing glance, there are smiles before they part one between the other, hands linking, fingers opening with the precision of a clock's mechanism moving until the hands again part. Continue.

D says that the sun will soon set and that we've come too far. We decide he is right, turn and head home, follow the new set of six. The ones we'd seen advance, face on, now have their backs to us, already well ahead; the ones we followed are already lost to the last glare of sun-fall, long shadows.

We turn our back to the sun. Walk like four Giacomettis. – His blue period, D says. – He never had a blue period ... only a lean skinny period. Join hands in shadows. – Make yourself into a bell, D says, son and father, – Make yourself into a twin tower D says, Dad and you, me the advancing aeroplane. – That's horrid. – A seagull, then – not really, it's my hand. – As if I didn't know. – I like walking with you, D says. I like the way our heads become conjoined. Our shadows, now so far ahead, look as if they have already slipped over the next mountain, as if we are approaching the forest with our one head rolling over spruce. The expected rabbits' ears and the windmill we make by crossing our arms. – Let's pull up our trousers, D says, pull them high to our waists, let the two of us make ourselves into Dad.

A & H's story

We have a house in Italy where we spend parts of the year. It was once a shell of a house, but we have spent years renovating it. A local woman who lives next door has had a vendetta against us for some time. She has sent threatening letters – well, more like notes really, anonymous, pretty unpleasant, name-calling – it was pretty obvious that she had sent them. Also things smeared on the walls. The letters began to arrive when her son, and the local builder we used, started messing us around and we had several disagreements with them over bills. We had to stop using him and then instead gave the work to a man who turned out to be the first builder's former business partner.

A short time after all this happened, I was at the house for a few days with some friends. Whenever I was there, there'd inevitably be problems with the water and electricity. It seems that this is normal in parts of rural Italy: nothing works – and the house is so isolated and still half-finished. On this occasion I was pleasantly surprised when we got there that everything seemed to be working okay. After a couple of days, something odd started to happen with the water pressure. Normally this was a sign that we were running out of water, but the cistern, the big water tank for storing water in the summer, and the well, were both full. We called in the plumbing people and they said something about the filters being blocked so they cleaned the main filter on the external pipes and they showed us how to clean the internal ones on the taps. This works by unscrewing a kind of grilled cap on the very end of the tap where water shoots out and cleans all the muck out. This still didn't solve the problem, though, so we got someone out who cleaned filters in one of the two boilers. They said that the filters were filthy and had lots of muck and fibres caught up in them.

Everything was fine for a day or two, but then the toilets stopped flushing – apparently they have filters on them too. We cleaned them out as best we could, and kept doing the same with the water taps, almost three or four times daily. Then we noticed that there was animal hair caught in them. Someone suggested a rat may have got into the well but it was impossible to see as the entrance was so narrow. Anyway, the problems continued. At some point someone suggested we get the well cleaned. The men we rang hoiked this big machine up the hill, something that looked like a big drill. When they began work we heard a loud sound of crunching and a gravely sound. The man pulled out what turned out to be a bag of bones, hence the crunching, and enough flesh for him to ascertain that it had been a cat. The man told us we were lucky not to have contracted typhoid and asked us if we knew anyone who held a grudge. He said that the opening to the well was so small that a cat could not possibly have fallen into it, that the cat would have to have been shoved down into the water either dead or alive.

The face seems to be a kind of sound, the sound of language evacuating its sense ...

To be in relation with the other face to face is to be unable to kill. It is also the situation of discourse.

Without a face what are we. Where are we?

Levinas

If I were to make a Photofit, from what?

I would sit there a long time with a series of eyes, mouths, noses, hairstyles like those books I'd buy for the children that came in three sections and we'd turn and turn the eyes, the hair, the lips, and make the man into a woman and a combination of each. A beauty spot – She's a looker, we'd laugh. Would I want you to be a looker? I wasn't expecting that.

If looks could kill...

Do I imagine you smiling, expect signs of ageing, a line over your eyebrow. Crows' feet. The now-healed gash where you once caught a stone.

A visitor without a face is not to know how to speak.

Even Frankenstein's monster had a face that grew to be cute over time, the flattened skull almost adorable and vulnerable, the way he wore his bolts and scars, slept badly, those dark circles under his eyes, weary fate. Like a head I made once while I was in art school, in what you might call my absurd period – when I painted head after head, no one I knew, no one knew why. A head made from rubber, made from scraps I found. Sheets of black rubber skin over foam, large woven stitches – it made my fingers bleed. I worked like a surgeon, sometimes as delicate as a seamstress, embroidering around lips and eyes, not knowing what I'd done. Sometimes the stitches were crude and untidy because the task was too hard. The face emerged slowly, my fingers bruised and split. The face seemed gruesome and twisted but it was mine and I loved him. I cut off some hair, tried to sew it to the scalp but it cheapened it, so I left the head bald. Carried it home under my arm. – Look what a monster he is! – a mother says to me as she scolds her child.

In your absence, with nothing more than a few miserable words from you thrown in our direction, a flurry of words toward you that you may never receive. I ask, – Do I create a monster out of you?

I shy away from the words *creation* and *monster*. The illusion of creation. Still on I go on, allow myself to continue with this two-headed thought, look up the word 'creation': *A dagger of the mind, a false creation, proceeding from the heat-oppressed brain* [Macbeth]; fearing this too dramatic, see that the root of the word monster comes from *monere*: warn. Portent: *A sign or warning that a momentous or calamitous event is likely to happen. Future significance.* And here's the contradiction, or maybe not: *2. (Archaic) an exceptional or wonderful person or thing. Origin: C16: from L. omen, token. Dark skies,* it says, *can be portent, a storm hitting, a silence, a portent of trouble. Foreshadowing, sign, indication, leads to foresee, forecast, foretell,* a right old knight on a wild steed hair blowing in the wind sword in hand. Roots of words also leading to *wonder, spectacle.* Berger saying: *what seems like creation is the act of giving form to what has been received* [...] *Paint as thick as ointment.* I shy away from reading too much into cards and teacups. I shy away from saying monsters are not just for Christmas.

You could say that Frankenstein's monster began with a good heart, a sound pair of lungs circulating good intentions into his being. It can begin well enough. Our motivations can be honourable, depending which side of which monster we are on. In our case, beginning badly enough – maybe our monster softens as time passes, you making one from En, me making one from you. En no doubt had his own model of monster, untold,

197

distinct from mine.

The heart begins it: words, fear, and a heart beating too rapidly. When you make a monster you have to begin somewhere. Monsters are also *fabulous creatures*, so the dictionary says. *Mythical. Abortion.* The monster owes you nothing but you forget that lesson. The monster never asked to be born. It was not his intention to be taken for a monster while he was taking you for the same. Maybe, once called up, the monster is content to just breathe, to stand, to open his eyes. It looks at you and wonders why it has to be so other, so unlike. It wants to be seamless, not bolted together. He thinks – do monsters think that way – he wants a better hairstyle, wants to be content with you when you eat dinner together. It wants to say – Pass the salt. Thank you. Please. A monster burps his appreciation into his napkin. It wants your eyes, not the ones you found for it. It wants to speak more than is permitted, but doesn't remember if it should add anything more than has been already uttered. Maybe it knows it has said enough, can never say enough. That whatever it says is clumsy, insensitive, something rehearsed yet too often blurted out. It gives you the impression it wants the house, the bed, the lover, the silverware or whatever cheap replicas you may have, but maybe instead it wants to be out of your story.

A monster begins with suspicion. Over time, you and the monster both grow discontent; you both begin to realise that you are capable of forgetting and remembering at the same time. That whatever short time you have had together, finally you will forget to remember one another, for reasons of health and wellbeing – and also because times change very fast, often without you realising; often, without you noticing, monsters go in and out of season and fashion. Once made they can too quickly become last year's look. Sometimes you have no more desire to spit names at it, to silently call it *Fool*, plan its demise, invent lines and scenarios for it. You do not use words like *extinction*: you just get bored with it, move on from it, that's how it is for both you and the monster, you both begin to outgrow one another, find different interests, books, stories to tell, remember a life together as something you cannot easily translate.

The theory goes that there are too many monsters brought into the world by too many unskilled minds, limp imaginations, humorous genetic fuck-ups we make in the evenings from over-anxious concerns, heartburn or insomnia. Sometimes environmental factors distract and kill the monster off before you are ready. Sometimes monsters are set free or escape while you travel, or choose a new rug, repaint the living room, find a new hat or job. Accept that only the fittest monsters survive. If the monster hadn't seen this written in your notebook, he wouldn't have panicked, or had his lucky break, depending on which way he looks at this. He wouldn't have taken off into the snow, to a place where you were forced to follow, to finish what you'd started, to allow yourself a little more time to properly say goodbye.

You still hear the heart beat from time to time if you listen close; if you are honest you are not sure whether the monster has gone, has moved seven doors down, or is hiding under the bed. Still, you prefer to continue with the idea that the monster has taken off through the snow, to the mountains, in keeping with historical texts. You saw yourself follow, fancied yourself as a bit of an explorer, a fictioneer; you wore thick clothes and protective eye-wear. You carried a pen and paper, protected from the weather in thick plastic. You carried a long stick like a lance, like the story that your father had once told you. You carried a box like the huntsman in *Snow White*. There is no mirror at home and even though the Queen knew her hearts you are trying not to think that far ahead or to get your genreless story mixed up with another genre, or any other stories that your father called out while he was carrying you on his shoulders, way back.

On the way through the snow – a monster doesn't always choose the best season to leave – you change back to the present tense, you call yourself names, you curse yourself for making him up in the first place, for letting him drag you out here so far from home. He, you; you, he – each cursing the other, cursing yourselves for drawing this out, each of you guilty of making the other up – whose monster is any longer whose? Until you see him in the distance – this makes your heart flutter in a way you hadn't expected, and your voice keen and precisely aimed calls after him – Monster! And you blush but he doesn't recognise his name; you run after him to find his hand. Monsters can be sentimental too: they can have a love of film, have an eye for a scene. He turns to wave like a pro, a touch of recognition, wanting more, wanting to touch. Monster, both of you say at once, rushing into an embrace, when inside you could no longer decide whether you wanted to take the heart from the monster, to pull the plug. He knew he would not be killed, only allowed to move on, to roam, to become his own monster, to be what he would in the world. The way you now, so briefly, look like the closest of friends.

Who could know what each of you wanted in that moment, through the gentle flurry of snow; how you looked like one body, with two heads twinned in white, faces looking out over each other's shoulder, looking far into your own opposite distances and directions. Soon to part and take your own routes, calling out, if, what, when…

Day Pages – Spain

The problem with flies increases as each day we come and go, open and close windows and doors, spend hours with the plastic swatters. Sickly oversized cans of spray that catch you in the throat. The sticky brown strips that dangle over the beds and kitchen and the sofa where Luke has set up camp downstairs. The bursts of swearing as one of us forgets, rises, hair or face stuck to the graveyard of dead and undead flies. I tell Luke the story: how, many years back, a boyfriend's mother died at her son's home, the home of my then-boyfriend's brother. She'd died while looking after her two-year-old granddaughter. The woman, far from home, who had travelled thousands of miles only weeks before, now lay collapsed in the bathroom, dying of a heart attack. The granddaughter was left sitting in the bathroom, toddling around the body while she waited for it to sit up again, to stop playing, to stop being so silly and dull, so frightening, obstinate and cold. Marlon in *The Godfather* comes to mind, playing with his grandson, falling among the tomatoes and dying in front of the puzzled child. If she could speak more, the child, she might have pointed at the grandmother slumped on the floor and said, – Wait until Mother gets home. Wait until I tell my father about you. Of course, having no idea if her mother or father would come home again.

At the funeral of the mother, who never became my in-law, there were so many flies that we had to make a special trip to the store to buy flypapers, treacly strips that unroll from what resembles a large shotgun cartridge. By the afternoon, post-service, the strips were so full of black bodies, twitching legs and wings struggling for life, that we had to remove them and replace them with new ones. Conversations throughout the afternoon seemed always to come back to the copious amounts Jack Daniels that the family members were drinking, those left alive, and the amount of flies gathered beside the dead.

In Spain, we decide that using jars to trap the flies will be more hygienic outdoors, where we eat in the evenings. Having eaten the conserves and the *mermelada*, we leave a little of the jam at the bottom of each glass jar and add in a mix of vinegar to keep away the bees. Make some jagged holes in the lid and add a little soap to the mix to prevent the seduced flies from saving themselves once they fall into the liquid. Some suggest urine, soda, banana, pieces of meat – there's even a small video Luke finds online, of a very earnest man making a fly-trap from a small baby-food jar, a plastic bag with a hole, water, and a dollop of his baby son's poop. The baby son makes baby noises while the man scoops the poop and says that if people don't have a baby they can use anyone's poop. No one volunteers, so we stick with mermelada, greengages, odd over-ripe jammy figs. And sure enough, the jars begin filling just as soon as we finish making them.

I have no idea if I could witness the death of a mammal with such acute observation, patience and no guilt, as we find ourselves counting the flies who lost their lives, those struggling on, the water thick already. Someone suggesting we must empty the traps daily to avoid the live flies using the dead as a raft.

I have no love for flies. People tell me all the time that a fly which finds its way into your home and persists is a dead person visiting. I always do everything I can to remove the dead person from the window. I give it a chance, but the dead are stubborn and have no need to rush off; where is there to go? Even when I trap it between the closed blind, stretch the window wide behind it, it stays, it knows. A jar works best. Imagine if they had jars for us. Big enough for our gluttony. At least we'd die, Luke says, full and satisfied. To be killed on an empty stomach would make it more of a tragedy.

~

There's a one-eyed cat that has taken to visiting each day, and that also visits the old house I can see from the gold room. I wonder if he used to live there. D has taken to feeding him small tins of sardines. This morning I found him chewing on some bird he'd dragged into the yard. The way he chews at the rather large black bird reminds me of the Goya we saw at the Prado, *Saturn Devouring His Son* – a deranged toothless cavern gobbles on the stump of a child, head gone. Saturn can neither stop nor go back, madness in his face, the disbelief while he goes on chewing, for fear, not tasting a thing of what he is holding arse-side out, the little legs of his boy. There is something about the way the cat turns his jaw left and right, the size, enthusiasm and strength of his bite, the small lapping tongue working between, rough and wet, that won't leave me long after I turn away. Either way, he continues to make strong bites left, right, upon the now-headless body of a large black bird, looking around with his good eye checking from time to time that no one is about to rob him – a moment I wish I hadn't noticed from the window.

Still, the birds continue to fill the sky, the small swallows we look forward to each day that punctuate the wires and washing-lines in the morning and evening, their colours brightened by the first hours, saturated in the last light. The fate of today's bird alongside the songs from small caged birds that decorate most of the walls and windowsills of the village houses here, that bring back the story of the canary we lost, our almost-forgotten Picasso. Not an original name – not that he complained. The tiny bird I felt the guilt of caging, consoling myself that he knew nothing of flight, nothing of that magnitude. Wanting to buy into the myth that he'd perish for sure if I freed him, set him loose to an expanse of inclement sky. If you opened the cage door there was always hesitation. One day, shortly before his death, while recording a small passage of my work, I unknowingly caught the bird on tape – he was singing to the sound of my voice. How he loved the rhythm of the written word, and loved music, opera, Maria Callas – Puccini in particular. My baby yellow canary sang much kinder notes than I could find. How he loved the feel of the sun, the air in his feathers. The taste of the bright leaves of the vine where, if the weather permitted, we'd leave his large square cage hanging – high up, we said, out of harm's reach. The walk we took one such warm afternoon was brief. Picasso. His head stolen, we assume by an absent cat. I shall never know the cat's colour, but I guess it was orange. Not our own cat, who at the time of our walk was surely asleep upstairs. He looked innocent enough, didn't lick his chops when I called the bird's name. Not guilty, he said, as he raised an eye bored by the ructions that loss brought on. There were no clues outside, only feathers blowing along the path, stuck to the minute plant hairs on my favourite shrubs. Our bird, lying at the bottom of his cage, a headless perfect yellow next to a single drop of red blood. He loved the tango best of all. We buried him hastily beneath the pine tree where our cat likes to sit, where the soil catches the warmth of sun and the pine needles make a soft bed. For some weeks we searched for the tiny head; thought of him when we broke into the centre of our boiled eggs.

Ciara's story

It started the day after I came back from the funeral of a close friend. It was December the 18th 1993, and I'd just received a letter through the post. I was sharing a house with a friend of mine. The letter arrived and I read it and my response was to go blank and think – what the hell is this. It didn't make any sense. I couldn't understand what it was talking about. I read it again and then thought, Oh, my god, this is a threatening letter. It was a threat to hurt my son and me, and to damage the property where we lived. I can't remember the details, the police have still got the letter and I don't want it back, and I haven't got a copy. It was a handwritten letter. It was anonymous, but over time I became aware of who it was from. I was a member of a parents' group at the time – I'm not any more – and my first response was to grab the letter – I still had a cup of tea in my hand – get in my friend's car and go with her to the centre. I didn't know what else to do. I went off to the centre and someone was there, they were very kind and said they'd find someone for me to talk to, but the trouble was that I was acting quite strangely at that point, and they didn't understand. I didn't know how to behave, but neither did they. These people weren't friends. I couldn't really tell them what I felt, because I didn't know what I felt.

The next thing I did was go to the police. A young woman constable came to the house to see me. She looked at the letter but they didn't seem to know what to do either. The police said useless things, like 'You seem a bit emotional about this'. At the time and for a long time afterwards I had no idea who had written the letter. There was a woman I knew who was a bit unstable and I thought it may have been her and that was the only thing I could suggest. The letter itself named someone I knew, a man I'd had a very close friendship with. They actually put in the letter his address and phone number.

What had happened eighteen months prior to my getting the letter, and I didn't connect it with the letter even then, was that I'd had my purse stolen, my cards stolen, my address book, and all my personal details that I kept in my space at work, all these things kept going missing. Much later on the security men at work even put in a little video camera in a box file. I work in a university and they put a video camera in my bay and filmed. But I didn't put any of that together with the letter writer. I don't know why, but it didn't occur to me.

In the letter the person said that they worked at the tax office and so had all this information on me. They said they knew where I lived and what my job was and how to get into my wages. They set up standing orders, as they had my bank details. They'd order clothes for me and always tick the size twenty boxes even though I am not anything like that size. Requests for information on wheelchairs, a threat of what was to come. And the bank didn't notice that it wasn't my signature on the things that were ordered. I have a list of all the companies this person ordered things from on my behalf. I got so many packages at home delivered to me, deliveries of things like china thimbles, furniture, clothing, anything they could think of. And I had to write to every company or phone them, which cost me a fortune, and explain that I'd been the victim of a hoax and to please send me the form that was used to set up this order. Many sent me the originals, and that way I gathered written evidence and got more and more handwriting. The person also tried to take out a loan in my name. It was only then that the bank contacted me.

About six months later I got another hate letter, very similar, probably more detail. At the time I was so worried about receiving mail that I'd take any letters I'd get round to a friend or into work to a colleague and I'd say, You open them. When I got the second letter the police did get more involved. The second letter was a continuation of what they'd said before, but this time it was more against my son. I tried not to tell my son too much, I kept it from him for a long time, he was only ten at the time and I didn't want to frighten him.

Once the police got more involved they flew to Northern Ireland because the man mentioned in the first letter lived there. My friend was, at the time, in another country and even though I told the police it was a waste of time and nothing to do with him, they disregarded that information and flew there anyway. I'd wanted them to get on with doing things like a handwriting analysis, which they were refusing to do. They told me that in order to make any charge based on handwriting analysis the police cannot use the letters alone, they have to have a sample of the person's handwriting that matches the handwriting in the letters, and they have to have witnessed that sample being written directly. They said they weren't prepared to interview or interrogate suspects, as really at that point I still didn't know who it could be; I still hadn't connected my things going missing at work with the hate mail.

In the office where I worked we all more or less had our own workspaces with a drawer at the front of the desk, but in a row of other workspaces. When the security camera was put in at work it filmed this guy that I worked with opening the door of the office, looking up and down the corridor to check he wasn't being seen, opening my personal drawer, taking out my things, looking at them and inspecting them. It was a man I'd worked directly next to. And the funny thing was, I'd told everyone I work with that there would be a camera put into my bay and they would be filming, and I told everyone because I didn't like the idea of spying on my colleagues. But as luck would have it, the day that I told them he was in a meeting and so by the time I got around to telling him, he had already done the deed. He hadn't taken anything, because by the time the camera was fitted there was nothing left to take, by then all my personal things had already been stolen, but he was on film having a good rummage through. When I told him about the camera being installed, I saw that his face dropped, and I said to him, – You seem to have a problem with that. Later the security department checked the film and we had a look at it. When I saw him taking my things I panicked and asked them to destroy it. I don't know why, but even then I didn't put the two things together, the letter and this; I wasn't thinking straight. When the tape was destroyed I later had no evidence.

This man was someone who had, in the past, wanted a relationship that I had not been prepared to have. I was nice to him at the beginning, but soon realised that things weren't right and backed off, and was very clear with him that I wanted nothing to do with him. He acted as if we were having a relationship and we weren't. He was very possessive. The police had said that they didn't think it was a woman, and they asked me had I any boyfriends in the past … and I remember looking at the handwriting and thinking, Oh my god, it is exactly the handwriting that I work with every day.

Despite working out who it was, the police were useless. I'd even been to my MP and I'd asked if the case could be moved to another police department to try and find someone who would deal with it more professionally. I did finally find a policewoman who was a little more helpful. By then I had a whole bin liner full of things that I'd been receiving through the door, evidence and samples I'd obtained from the various mail-order catalogues, but she'd still insisted that it was not a criminal offence. At that time there were no anti-stalking laws and my MP knew of no way to help, saying there were no laws he knew of that applied to my case. And so I told the policewoman, – If this is not a criminal offence then I am going to do exactly the same thing to him. I actually wouldn't have, because it would have taken too much effort and time. The police did then visit him at home. They explained to him that a woman he was working with was being threatened, and whatever was happening shouldn't be happening any more, and that it had to stop. They said that they couldn't arrest him, or accuse him, or maybe more, that they wouldn't. The dribbles still came through the post for a while, things he'd ordered on my behalf, things he'd set up before the police spoke to him. But after their visit the letters did stop.

When I found out who it was, managers at work refused to accept that my colleague had done this, so I walked out one day and said I am not coming back until you sort this out. I was at home for three months. When I did then get called in for a meeting, I got a union rep, and the guy who had written the letters took his wife in to support him at the meeting. I discovered that she was involved as well. One of the phrases in the letter was, I have just moved here and I am going to follow you everywhere. I can't remember the sequence of events, but she ended up using that exact phrase from the letter and I suddenly realised that she was part of it too. I didn't know who'd done what, whether she'd given him the ideas and he'd written it down, or whether she had written it for him. And although I resolved it for myself, I don't think the people I worked for ever really believed me or understood. When I went back to work I demanded that they move me to another department. The man who wrote the letters never showed any reaction at all. He never refuted what I'd said, didn't take any action, didn't sue me.

It changes everything. Even now I don't open the post in a normal way; I am very cautious about who I give my personal details to. You start off with this one piece of paper, but the consequences of that ... I don't really think even the letter-writer can begin to know what that means for you. I don't think they can ever realise what they do.

D is explaining different ways to defend myself.

It's not the first time since your letter arrived that he's mentioned this.

– If someone tries to grab hold of your arm, he says, and tries to stab you … he demonstrates in the kitchen at home, my arm twisted. We are laughing, but the more he grabs my arm the more nervous I become that he will push it out of its socket, not meaning to, just because of his tallness and strength and exuberance. – Always fall onto an attacker, D says. Always fall into the direction he is pulling, fall onto him, surprise him, and give him your full weight when he least expects it. – Try it, D says, lifting me off the floor into the air and into his arms where I dangle. Chris Crudelli, he tells me, is a young guy who is trained in martial arts, and is often on TV. Hugo and D drag me to see the clips and explain how Chris Crudelli used to break his own hands to strengthen them, used to break bricks over his hands, smash his hands into walls to break his knuckles and calcify them. We watch the video of Chris knocking various celebrities to the ground.

This, just the day after Hugo finished three days of filming for a knife-crime film; Hugo playing the part of the kid who persuades his friend to carry a knife for protection. In the film, the friend and Hugo's character look up knives on the internet, decide in the end to just take one of his mother's large kitchen knives. Hugo tells me how he got friendly with the woman on set whose job it is to apply the fake blood to the bodies and the knives. How she'd explained to him about the woman who supplied the blood, the woman who has the job of making fake blood for a living. Fake blood and fake flesh. The guy who was stabbed, Hugo says, had to have makeup to make him look pale and deathly, had to bite on a capsule of fake blood. He had a pump and a tube under his shirt so at the time he fell they could activate the pump so that the fake blood could begin soaking his clothes. – So there's this woman, he says, who wakes up every day to make fake blood. I bet she laughs while she does her work. I thought the woman who told me about her was making her up, he says, as if she's not real, but I believe she is real because otherwise where would the fake blood come from. But she's like a myth, and you say to yourself, Mmm, that's good, like Father Christmas… No, not like Father Christmas.

The language of knives we'd had to research just weeks earlier in preparation for his film. The coincidence of the time, of my writing to you, of you writing to En, my fear of knives heightened. My fear that if you came calling the knife would be your chosen weapon … rope, candlestick, lead pipe.

– Somehow it helps, Hugo says, to look at these things, like facing your fears, that's what people say isn't it, face your demons. – It helps? – They are beautiful, he says, I love knives. *In Elizabethan times,* Hugo reads, *it was customary for women to have their own knives. To wear them proudly in public, to carry them to display wealth, a pair of agate hafted knives, sheath with woven cover.* We stare at the details of the haft close up, silver filigree balloon pummel. *Collection knives, novelty, brand, kitchen, world fair, fair trade, pocket, a collection can be a source of great entertainment. Working knives, bread, meat and butcher's knives, hunting and fishing knives. The beauty of wedding knives, a canteen of … an urn that can hold up to sixty … Beginning with the history of eating utensils. Knives used as weapons, adapted for the table. Table use: narrow, sharply pointed to spear the food and then raise it to one's mouth. In 1669 King Louis X1V of France, concerned at the amount of fights that ensued around the table, the number of deaths, declared all the pointed knives on the street or on the dinner table illegal, had all the points ground down to reduce the violence.*

I hadn't associated our name with the knife before, not really. The irony of that; in all those years I hadn't really given it any thought, had thought no more about cutlery than the sets my parents were given on their wedding day. People don't get sets like that any more. My mother would keep the boxes in the dresser, and inside them were velvet or satin spaces in the shape of the knives, forks and spoons, a series of small velvet cuts where each set of implements would be held in place. I used to spend time with those boxes, sneak them out sometimes when I was on my own. Unwrap each piece from its tissue paper. My favourite was the largest set; the cutlery was made in the design of seashells, large serving spoons like scallops, held to mouth and ear, but they were silent spoons untouched by lips, food, neither saltwater nor suds.

– It says here there were Sunday knives, forks for cheese and cake, lemon jelly, wheat porridge, chocolate cream sucket spoons – forks were slow to catch on. – Let's look up some proper knives, Hugo says: assassin's knives. We should delete everything we look up as we go – clear the history… People watch, you can get into trouble, get arrested for looking these things up. – That's nonsense, and if anyone comes I'll tell them we are just researching. – They all say that! … *Cold steel knives, Sog, Kershaw, Gerbe*, great names! *Emerson, Buck, Boxer.* That one's got a push-button locking system, *speed master drop point, light-weight features, lustrous brass butt. Handsome!* It says it's *rugged, strong. Silent! Made from Tru-sharp surgical steel.* Wait until you see this … *fast, aggressively deadly. Offers 'big knife' cutting.* – I can't stand these. Let's look up some nice old ones again, like these, the ones with the bone and mother of pearl handles. *People were expected to carry their own knives to others' houses and if they forgot them they'd have to eat with their hands.*

– In the film I was in, the kid wrapped the huge kitchen

knife in a yellow duster and shoved it down his joggers ... or his eating pants! The wonders of elastic giving way to three junk meals per day plus whatever weapons.

– Let's look up butterfly knives. – What, for killing butterflies? – Don't be daft. Home protection from butterflies, just in case you get some swarm of killer butterflies rushing at you in the garden and you need to take a knife to ward them off... A *butterfly knife, it says, has a handle that splits into two parts like wings that close around the knife when it's not in use. It encases the blade.* That's the most wicked idea ... Let's put in 'combat knife'... This is a beauty... *Combat, proven sleek, genuine stag, etched and filigree bolsters, comes with a velveteen gift bag. Created for special CIA operations* – the knife, Mert, not the bag! – I don't think the CIA had velveteen bags ... *Captures the mystique of the fixed blade, length: 7.5 inches.* Imagine that being stuck in you. – Let's click back to the cutlers... Love poems, look at that! Etched onto the blades. Couplets. *My love is fixt, I will not range, I like my choice, it will not change.* – That's a crap poem. *The art of grinding blades caused the death of many cutlers who would sit astride a wooden 'horsing' to hold the blade as the wheel was turned by foot or water power, inhaling the grinding dust. Making steel knives, the material is first cut into strings like spaghetti, heated to 2,000 degrees Fahrenheit, and forged together with a hammer with over 300 tons of force, heated again and dipped into an oil bath to make it hard.* – Spaghetti, imagine that. Let's get back to the butterflies. *Add to cart,* it says... *A tool that can serve your grandchildren from the cave to the cosmos.*

Today I let myself wander without thought in the direction of the museum again.

Since your letter's arrival, and now well beyond that time, the museum mollifies and distracts – the scale of the place, a place to hide and write even though there are times when I admit to self-consciousness; the awkwardness of the gaze, the glazed scrutiny of security guards, the odd woman like myself wandering idly between paintings. The far-off echo of children never changes, the tone and depth of male voices, the squeak of rubber soles on light oak floors.

Today it was the chicken that caused me to stop. Many rooms on and in, can you believe it, a chicken stops me dead. I can never anticipate what will cause such hesitation, cause me to stand or sit awhile. Frans Synders' *Studio of Paul Rubens*, the plaque says. *1579-1637, The Poulterer's Shop.* Poulterer, a word I enjoy, a word that hasn't existed in my vocabulary – these days all carrion are mixed together. *Oil on canvas 1612-1615. Allocated by HM Government in lieu of inheritance tax 1998.* The elderly shopkeeper in the painting stares intently at the kitchen maid as she looks through the poulterer's produce, pointing out what she desires. *In Antwerp at that time such senses had veiled erotic content,* it says. The Flemish word for bird, I learn, *vogel,* has phallic associations, while *vogelen* (to bird) is slang for sexual intercourse. *Synder's specialism was still-life painting, focusing on detailed depictions of birds, vegetables and game.* Among all the birds, foul, partridges, pigeons, are artichokes and onions, sausages hung, stuffed with herbs. There's an elaborate cauliflower and beneath, squashed into one corner, a rabbit. His head at the bottom left of the image; he is looking up at me, upside-down, his ears toward me. He barely looks dead, his legs reaching up towards the cauliflower. The pantry is full of gleaming copper pots, pewter jugs, lamps and a brass mortar and pestle. The kitchen maid is holding two chickens, still alive, and she points to another held in a basket. Her arms are solid and red as if she's been delivering too many children, washing too many pans, clothes, and the innards of birds. While the man – who could be her father, but obviously isn't – stares at her as if he would like to pluck her. The description implies he has other matters on his mind, but I am not convinced. His tight ringleted hair, full beard … maybe I am naive. Whose voice is this? It's not easy to stay here, to look. I almost want it to be quieter than it already is.

– That's Jesus, a young voice says, pointing at a painting to my back. That's Jesus, Mum. Mum. He's behind you. There's so many Jesuses here, Mum …

… reminding me of the well-dressed middle-aged woman I'd passed on the way here, in the subway: she was standing on a small buckled suitcase, her body swaying, singing so sweetly, – Jesus is alive. He lives. Lives.

I'm not maudlin here; in some ways it's a comfort. The space, the anonymity and, despite my original theme, long abandoned to a letter, there are no windows here. Once you are deep inside the innards of the place there are only guards, moments of complete stillness, only the whirr of the humidifier, the windows of insects, jewels and stuffed animals, yellow glass eyes, the painting I have claimed as mine – even though I really had no interest to begin – no more than a chicken calling me. Do chickens know when they are about to die? Surely. Looking is so painful sometimes that I am eager to retreat to the tea-shop. No one stops you or asks you what you are doing here. If I were to map the areas I wander they would be very few. I give the impression of wandering, but finally I don't go that far from home. Home. I keep close, weeks gone by since I came looking for The Kiss.

It's the gift shop that reminds me of my sons, the souvenir shop that is bigger now than when we first came here together.

It's illuminated like a Christmas decoration, like the tiny house I used to put on the tree. The decoration I always got to choose each year from the box that had been locked away in the garage. The house, snow walls that sparkled. It had four foil windows, some gold for the rooms that were lit up, red for the rooms that were in semi-darkness or where the fire burned low. The door was always a little ajar and there was a wreath with berries. A doormat. The roof laden with snow and the robin keeping warm near the chimney where the smoke came out in puffs of already greying wool. The little house I'd put at eye level so I could peer at it and imagine who was home. Father on his way, carrying home the tree he had chopped down for Christmas. Bringing home the plucked goose. A little drunk – Father, not the goose. Mother stayed sober. Played piano badly but no one much cared. It was always Christmas Eve inside the little house. There were always tangerines in the bowl. The dog slept most of the day. He had a velvet bow tied to his collar for the festive season. That evening the children would find it hard to sleep and their parents would have sex quietly after nibbling at the mince pie – allowing the dog to munch on the carrot top.

It's full of small boys, the souvenir shop: boys battling their way out with plastic swords and Roman helmets. It's the tea-shop I like best of all. It has brown leather sofas. Brown leather sofas have become an epidemic these days, but they safely allow me to hide in a corner, to sink into hiding and watching. It's the simple choices we make with tea that touch me. Which kind. To sugar or not. How milk affects the temperature, colour, and the time you must wait before you gulp. There's the supping and the motion, a man rubbing his hands, lifting the pot, moving it slightly as if that is important. He's ordered the same fruit cake as me. You could say nothing happens here but looking, the choice of sitting or standing, what to do with a serviette, postcard selections – the tea never lasts long enough when you drink alone. The man stirs his tea with his spoon and his eyes fill with memory, the small cake dunked, another Proustian moment. There are people who really like to look at you directly, and people who merely shoot you a glance. The light here is pink. A man over there won't talk to his son. He's staring at the boy's food, not his face. The man picks up his spoon. If I could have such warmth for a spoon – just the word, spoon. Rebel more. Speak to him about the way he stirs. The man doesn't look well. Stirs his tea for as long as his memory lasts, then moves on to the next image. Then he's gone, his tea not really touched. Replaced by two women. The man picks up his child and bounces him on his hip. I remember that way of sticking out my hip to hold a child. The way the women talk together, mimic each other, the delicacy of hands, drink without a word, balance a baby and a tray at the same time. The way children bounce when they run where no running is allowed. Where is she going ... where is there to go. One of the women wears a white glove as if she's hurt her hand. I want to be close enough to hear their secrets. To smell the buttered toast on the children's faces. I think it's time to go, without seeing The Kiss. The Kiss still hidden away somewhere in the bowels of the place, covered, bound up in darkness and silence ... to be lost together like that. Like the two women over there – not the ones gossiping beside me – the two older women over there, also sitting in complete silence, drawing together so at ease that they have almost forgotten to look at one another, but look instead into the same distance, draw, rub out, draw over, continue; don't compare, or ask, or peek at what differs in what they see. Maybe they are sisters. They look alike. I might have preferred The Kiss. Now I am here I cannot leave. They will not kiss each other, these sisters, not now, nor think of it until they part; if part they will. I am curious to know what the women draw. That pattern of darkness I need to see; need not.

En's other story – letters to Zambia

My first-ever trip abroad was to Africa in 1968. I was nineteen years old, and got a job as an agricultural research assistant in northern Zambia, in a town called Kasama. It was two years before I came home again, and the hardest adjustment was not to arriving in Africa as a teenager, but to arriving home again. My first impression of Britain after two years away was when I looked out of the bus as it drove from the airport at 7am, dark and raining, and I saw all these men cycling to work at factories, their canvas lunch-bags over their shoulders. I determined then that I would go back to Zambia, and by 1973 I'd saved up enough money to buy a one-way ticket, plus £200 cash, and I arranged to meet up with old friends in Kasama. The wife of the guy I stayed with was the daughter of the town's mayor. I stayed in their house for about three months and all was well. I met up again with all the people I'd known from my earlier time there. K and I were always looking for ways to make some money and at one point I gave him my £200, which was all the money I had, to buy some cows. We were going to butcher them and sell the meat to schools. We ended up on a kind of island in a lake in the middle of nowhere to buy the cows, and spent a whole day in this eerie place butchering dead flesh. There was no part of the beast that the Zambians did not use. I spent hours that day ankle-deep in water, squeezing the shit out of what seemed like miles of intestines, and rinsing them out in the lake. Hanging up around the lake were many fishing nets, and I went up to one of the nets to touch it and my friend screamed at me, – Don't touch the nets; if you do you'll never be able to leave this place. Superstitious nonsense, but I didn't touch the nets.

At the time I was there, the Chinese were building a railway line from Dar es Salaam on the Tanzanian coast to Lusaka, the

Zambian capital. I had flown to Dar es Salaam from London, and I spent two days hitchhiking to meet my friends at the Zambian border at a preappointed date and time. I'd spent one night sleeping in a ditch by the side of the road in the middle of the bush without any fear, still young and naive and full of the excitement of being back.

This was a time when Zimbabwe was still Southern Rhodesia, and it was my misfortune that some white Rhodesian terrorists blew up the railway line not far from where we were living in Kasama. The police were looking for any white person they could arrest who did not have a legitimate reason for being in the area, and although there were a lot of white Rhodesians and South Africans working in Kasama, I was the only person around who was not gainfully employed. I was just there on a visitor's permit. After the railway line was blown up, the local police – not the ordinary police, more like the local MI5 – were frantically trying to find these people and arrested me. I was lucky at least that I was staying in the mayor's daughter's home with her and her husband, but they took me to the police station anyway and interrogated me. They said that they had been observing me for a while and had been intercepting all my mail. I didn't even know I'd had mail until I saw all the letters on the officer's desk. When I left the UK I also left a girlfriend behind, and she had been writing me letters. We were both very young. She knew that I had been really unhappy and bored back in Britain, and how much I'd wanted to go back to Zambia, so when I left she wrote me these really innocent letters. In one of the letters she sent she said, – I'm glad you've found what you were looking for. The men who'd arrested me had underlined in red pen certain sentences all through her letters, including that particular sentence, twisting the meaning around so that they kept asking me: What was it you found … They didn't actually beat me up or anything, but they were really threatening, maybe because they knew I had no connection to Southern Rhodesia and was staying with the Mayor's daughter.

But all around the room in which I was being interrogated were pictures of other people who had been tortured; there were handcuffs and clubs and all sorts of instruments of torture around the walls. They kept on and on about this letter and what it was that I had found, asking me what I was doing over here. I tried to explain that they'd got it all wrong, that she just meant that she hoped I'd found happiness, but they were saying, – We know this woman, we've spoken to Intelligence in your country and we know this woman is a secret agent. They were determined to try to get me to admit to something.

In the end they put me under house arrest. I suspected later that the Mayor might have had something to do with it, a way to get rid of this nuisance white guy who was dossing at his daughter's place, because for some strange reason they didn't take my passport off me. There was this terrible three-weeks period where I imagined all kinds of horrors happening. I knew I had to get the hell out of the country, and that at any time they could come back, torture me, shoot me, do anything to me. The problem was, I didn't have any money, because I had given my £200 for the cows and couldn't now get a ticket home. There was a lot of tension between my friend and me because I knew he did not have the money, or that he'd blown it. I kept telling him that I had to get that money back and leave. He was trying to borrow money off various people and in the end this one guy lent him the money and I got the £200, caught a bus really early in the morning, and sneaked all the way down south to the capital where I managed to get a flight and come home.

D and Hugo arrive home with a series of photographs taken of them standing beside a post box they came across while visiting their aunt.

My favourite image is one of them taken from a distance either side of the box, backs to the camera. In their motion, giving the box a last glance, they are both advancing and already departing, both arriving and passing by. The box slants between them like a miniature Tower of Pisa. D explains: the box is situated next to a public telephone that has become a well-known site where addicts meet and do their business. The Post Office decided to move the box, since workers emptying it were being injured with needles dumped inside with the letters. Locals, not wanting to lose their precious box, wrapped the pillar in garlands of flowers and leaves, topped it with pink roses, stuck tiny postcards and children's drawings to it, scribbled red imitations, poems and messages sellotaped to its body. *Rest in Peace – a last post ode …* Each new line by *The Bard of Windmill Hill – Bye–Bye Boxy, Boxy Bye-Bye –* spelling out

L
E
T
T
E
R;

his *Benediction for a Box … Although we may feel madness/ Let's let this box depart/ Let letters of our sadness/ Be posted on its heart.* A posting of W.H. Auden … *And none will hear the postman's knock/ Without a quickening of the heart./ For who can bear to be forgotten …* followed with a footnote: *Please attach your love letters to the post box below.*

Hugo tells me that he's never received a letter. He says that people these days don't ever get them. – What would you do with it, anyway, if you did get one? – you'd have to put it some-where. If you write an email or an MSN message to someone or a text then you can just delete it. Hugo says that the only time he ever wrote a letter was in school, as an exercise, formal and informal, a question of tone, address, which sides to put what, how to begin, sign off, all that stuff they make you go over and over – it's enough to put you off letters for life. A kid in my class didn't even know what stamps were; he thought they were stickers.

I tell him that, with the exception of your letter, the pleasure of receiving a letter through the post never changes for me. Despite loving my emails, I still prefer to get a letter – especially if it is handwritten in ink, the trace of the person beginning with the envelope. I always hold onto it for some time before opening. I make tea, find the right chair, the right time: it needs time. The first reading may be swift, with quick calculations. This begins with the envelope, how fat it is – the fatter the better, normally – yours aside. What does the person have to say? Check the number of pages – if they have written on both sides obviously that makes the letter longer. And so the anticipa-tion of the number of pages, the size of the handwriting, how many words per line.

Someone, knowing I am writing the book, sends me a story about love letters she received some years ago. Well, she wants to tell me more but can't talk about it at the moment. She says she can't yet tell me how important those letters were to her. She also sends a postcard of Vermeer's *Woman in Blue*, reading a letter, the woman in the painting turned to the side, her pregnant belly telling its own story. The woman is clutching the letter, having only just opened it, having only just begun to read. You can see that she is trying hard to comprehend what it says. Maybe she doesn't want to. A message scribbled on the back of the image reads that the woman in blue hasn't yet got to that part: the heart of the letter, the rejection, the hurt, the incomprehensible, the thing that will change everything for her, for the baby. Maybe a different future begins with this letter, or were we being pessimistic in expecting bad news?

When I began talking to others about your letter and when others began to share their stories with me, I asked people to send me not only their stories of threats, but also to send examples of the most beautiful letters they'd ever given or received – something extraordinary. No one opted for the latter. People seemed only to have an urgency to tell me of the threatening letters. Some sent me the actual letters they'd received, and this touched me very much. I became the keeper of the letters. I am yet to meet someone who owns up to *sending* a threat letter, apart from the obvious *Dear Johns*. Maybe there is a threat in all letters. The want, the call to reply: Now listen to me…

I haven't got to the killers yet… [Beckett]

While tidying up my bookshelves I come across a book that someone once gave me but which I don't think I ever read, called: *Why do Women Write More Letters Than They Read?* Chapter One: *Why do men tend to keep love letters in files along with other correspondence?* – Back to Hugo's – and where would I keep such letters if I ever got any? *Whereas women,* it continues, *often keep them in their clothes.* I keep mothballs in my clothes, Paracetamol, coins and pens. En carried your letter around in his clothes, in the inside pocket, that dark secret place over the heart. I still won't read the book *Why do Women …*; to analyse all those reasons why men and women do what they do bores me to death these days …

I don't remember the first letter I wrote; maybe it was to mother when she was briefly in hospital. I know I used paper that was often coloured lilac, pink, or gold. Some of the paper had faint pictures around the edge that created a frame to emphasise the blank space that was just waiting for you to fill it. Some had small landscapes at the bottom, or creatures sketched at the corners. Watermarks – I'd forgotten those. That was quality. A crest. Hidden faces. Letters embossed. The word *embossed* is enough to fill you. Letters that were scented, most often with violets. If the scent wasn't strong enough, you'd add some of your own cheap version, or your mother's if you could get hold of it, being careful to spray the perfume into the air and then move the paper in the direction of the mist so as not to stain the letter with drops of wet perfume, not to expose to the recipient that you cared enough to add more smell than the manufacturers had already, to leave no telltale stains or smudges or droplets. If you wanted the scent to come from you in a more intimate way, first you'd spray or dab the scent into your neck or wrist, give it time to warm and reach its full potential, then carefully rub the letter over your skin. Same with the envelope, except when you wanted the odour to rise from the opening tear, that distinctive smell inhaled for seconds cautiously, deeply – you know they are already holding the letter to their nose, before reading, after reading. My loved one, they say, their face wrapped in what has seeped onto the page as you wrote: the effort, the ache, the *missing you* ... Fleeting moments before only the words remain; smell, the least reliable most transient of our senses.

Back then, the letters I'd write were twenty-pagers, sometimes double-sided. I have for sure excelled myself with you, lost count of where we now are, how many hundreds of pages in and still somehow we go on. People said they loved getting the letters I sent them, but maybe they were just being kind. Is this how writing began in me, with those first Dear listeners who seemed genuine enough, both in their own replies and sentiments, alongside their commitment to reading whatever I could gather and digress myself into, those old big-frocked, big-bloomered letters. Yes, I had to take it that those Dear ones weren't bored. In turn, I admit that there were times when I'd feel disappointed by the feeble attempts my pen-pal would make, someone I never met, someone you imagine a pro, eager for whatever challenge a twenty-pager might present, a pen-pal who you imagined was wholeheartedly committed to the word and the challenge. But in truth, she never got beyond four or five pages of rather dull news, plain lined unscented paper, nothing to raise to the nose or last the volume of a mug of tea. Her letters aside, onionskin was my favourite. Was it after all blue, as I recall? Blue words on blue pages, simple enough to sky the day, words that could be seen from both sides if you held the pages to the light, words backwards, *sdrawkcab*. The pull and slant of elaboration, gobbledygook: what a word in itself. The gobbling familiar backchat of words reversing from right to left.

I haven't tried this with your letter, haven't yet held it up to the light, looked at the words rising East, heading West; your words of course typed, machine-made, your XXXs that would surely remain untouched by any backward glance. When held to the light, all those haphazard Xs penned from whatever past conferrer or gossipmonger I was in cahoots with at the time, were more open to change, their kisses pregnant, drunk, defiant, some unfinished, undone, shy, or showing off. Either way, kisses stray as pretty as a line of paper chains, hand-crafted among those unreadable loops of language I would stare up and into, those reversed words, kisses lit up, the patterns they made. I would revel in those onion-skinned strings of words made new in the way I sometimes try to hear my own language as if I were a stranger. Do you do that, on the bus, try everywhere to hear others as strangers? – myself abroad. Someone once telling me that the sound English makes to a person who can't speak the language – well, had momentarily for him at least sounded like *wishy-whishy* … like clothes wish-washing. Suds everywhere. Imagine!

As you arranged the letter to En – yes, as always back to your letter, when in so many ways we've already wandered so far from those early corners, concerns and questions, such a spell and sentence of time since the letter was first placed in the red box, carried to the feather bed, but I forget so much – did I already ask? Yes, if you read the words out loud as you wrote, rewrote, revised, honed; if you read the words you wrote quietly to yourself, or to whatever stray was about, in whatever voice you could summon… How many false starts did you make from you to him, from me to you? There's a stubbornness to continue, for now at least. For me at last to exhaust myself in the subject of you, your letter, for a moment, all the letters I had ever received and sent piled high in my memory. Although most by now are forgotten, as for sure yours too will fade into the now-when-was-that, as time passes, as it surely does and will with the weather and the mail and the number of postmen that have come and gone in the time I have already spent writing to you, this mixed old stewpot, burgoo, pot-au-feu, all I can muster each day in this meandering retort that will surely go unseen by you. I am trying neither to judge nor to provoke. How many days are there left between us? I forget to ask, finding myself instead counting and checking and scrutinising, deleting, putting back, each day, each line to you read out loud, altered again, readjusted, underscored, under erasure…

She read his letter out loud several times, too many times. She read her reply even harder. She gave her reply hell, gave his letter the once-over and over. Read aloud. Read out loud. Something they repeat, underline and reiterate in all good – or, come to that, run-of-the-mill – writing classes. I've done it myself. Passed on whatever tired tips I had to those young eager beginners. Do more than whisper in your head, I've said. Project like a beam of light, like an arrow. Give any reply passion. Give it your all. The ear cannot be fooled, unlike the failing eye misted with floaters. We rarely settle in one place. Glasses on or off. The ear is another matter, a matter of balance, dual action. Listen! A lone voice is filling an absent ear. What belief. What nerve. We have to begin somewhere, people say, but I was never very strong on geography.

Still, I try to vary my range as I read, read aloud to you. My voice, always elaborating, still stutters from time to time, more often laughs at itself trying out accents, trying to find *the right aggregate of words*, slow beat, tap dance, a voice trying to forget the familiarity of its home address, to lose the sound of its day-to-day. The naiveté, when maybe after all, all I can offer is home. Finally, all I have tried to protect, the place I feared you'd entered, would return to, come back to, cease, finally, *is yours*. Here. Take it. Take it in the voice. Come home as you listen to me read. Hear the voice greet you. Clear its throat. Launch itself toward you. So soon: the impulse to step outside, unbolt the door, open the windows; there's little hesitation now, the voice flies off before I even said *begin*. Off it goes again. Ah, the mess of countries I end up with as I read aloud. The mishmash of voices crossing thousands of miles in one reading, the range of landscapes and food that could be eaten as we cross through the lines made in your direction. From page to page, over the course of so many fences jumped, a voice loses all bearings, all sense of where it's come from. Not that it forgets what is left of its family tree, but the more it continues, goes on and on until ...

Does a voice know any longer where it is headed, did it ever, should it know; a voice that doesn't know any longer what mother duck or stray donkey to follow. Toppling on a chair for misspelling. If a river without water is not technically a river, is a voice without a listener not to know how to speak? Write it down! A voice reading aloud in whatever bravado, in whatever fake Gucci, Italian mix, wool blend decides to slip up on the day, unreliable, uncharted lands. Laugh more. Get out more. Get louder. Hoping the postman won't call when my voice is at its strongest, its most absurd. I have not yet read your words to En in any accent except the one I have but don't hear. Maybe letters are different. Provoke a different persona. Don't hesitate here. Maybe letters come out of a different set of relations altogether; whatever family is found lurking in the vocal cords, normal elastic, I'm not so sure of anything here, the voice says. Yes, imagine my words to you read out beginning in a strong exaggerated Scottish accent, ending in a mix of Russian-Romanian. I cannot assume your country of birth, your history, your bloodlines, laughter and lifelines. What accent do you have, what languages can you speak, what silent pauses between sentences, what ash or maple or monkey puzzle, what more exotic palm might shade your tone; what depth your voice, what vowel sounds, what Southern drawls ... we all do it, voices put on like feathered hats, blonde wigs: Tippy again. Already covered, she sneaks up on me in her green suit.

Speak up, I hear someone call.

Unusually disturbed by the sound we make on tape.

At the museum, I find myself drawn to a painting of a rather bleak mountaintop.

Sky full with snow, a peak of snow that stands out across the room, I follow the snow, the paint applied so thickly, the strokes so visible you could touch the gesture, too gloomy to write about today. Deciding I am, after all, in no mood for a dark winter. Finding myself instead before an image made of grass. The texture is welcome among all this paint. The texture of a doormat like the ones that have Welcome written on them, or No Place Like Home … a stencilled umbrella, raindrops, a joke or two. In this case: *Bull's Head,* Heather Ackroyd … *Grass and Hessian on Board*.

When I came here today, I'd been searching the rooms for a cabinet of mourning stationery I remembered reading about, distracted instead by the paintings, sidetracked by the bull, the bull in not one but several different places. As if I had called him up, as if by piecing together the notes I'd made on the letter and the stationery I was trying to find here today, the bull had charged forth, pushed its snout into my pages and reminded me that maybe it was time also to attend to the story of the bullfight.

At the end of our holiday in Spain, we'd all decided, rather impulsively, that we would go to the corrida for the first time: the circle of yellow grit where we'd witness Hemingway's *Death in the Afternoon* – or in our case, death in the early evening. The knives I'd so feared now stuck into the body of not one, but too many bulls. But I'll get back to that later…

At the museum, some Spanish students who happen to be passing and happen to be Spanish tell the attendant guarding the bull's head that they are in Britain on an exchange. I listen to them chatter excitedly in Spanish, knowing they have no notion that I am sitting here trying to order the notebooks I brought back from their homeland, what came to be known

229

as my *Day Pages*; wanting to share the story but not knowing how to explain the nature of your letter that propelled this reply into being. There is nothing to indicate that the bull's been on my mind, as if my thinking of him, my trying to write about him, has again called him up… Here, among an exhibition of landscapes, mostly hills, old ruins, women on horseback, small figures among mountains and streams, extremes of weather and washing – here, the bull stands alone and stands out. I don't really understand what he is doing here. Only the tenuous link that he is made of grass among a gallery of landscapes. I am willing to accept that I am glad to see him, even though from this angle and this proximity I cannot see much more than a blur, a suggestion of bull.

Two of the Spanish students stand back from the bull after a brief inspection of the seeds fallen into bottom of the box that houses him, a box fronted by glass so that their smiling reflections mingle with the bull's efforts to look fierce. They photograph the bull and I wonder – can he be photographed? One of the students explains that the bull's image was made by projecting light through various negatives onto a vast grassy canvas; where there was more light the grass grew greenest, where starved of light it took on a yellow tinge. If I move to the right I can see the beginning of the bull's eye, a nostril flaring, but from this angle and this close up he doesn't seem at all ferocious. No more than a scared baby. The way the first bull had been in the corrida we witnessed, sweet, unnamed, trotting after the taunting *peones* as if he wanted only to play.

I move back to touch while the students argue over him for a while, call out with laughter, – Torro … torro… They take more photographs. I believe that nothing of this bull will show itself on film. As I step back he comes into focus, his virility emerges, neck muscles, ears still intact. The room curves and from here I can see nothing of the bleak snowy peak I began with, faltered over and left. A party of schoolchildren sits on the floor and crayons the bull to life with black thick enthusiastic marks that look angrier than he is. Most give him golden horns that I have failed to see. People point at him, circle him. I can tell that most are fond of him. The more I allow myself to stare hard at this bull, the stronger he gets. On their backpacks the Spanish students have written, *I am Spanish but you are not ...*

What I love about museums is the mishmash of cabinets you find close to each other, regardless of the narrative they try to sustain. Sometimes no more than a short walk takes you from beast and castrating tools through traction engines, ploughs and farmers smocks; from the eagerness of overfilled rooms and shrill voices to the silence of your own steps in the shadowy half light; from a room full of costumes, bonnets, perfume bottles, cigarette cases, shoes and fans, handbags and opera glasses into a wall of embroidered maps and obituaries, a small framed picture of Adam and Eve made from silver and gold threads – how to embroider god, so happy in this image, happily casting out the couple as if he were a Vaudeville comedian. God, jumping from a cloud like the cow jumping over the moon. He's almost chewing on a cigar. Laughing so much at the apple, the distress, Adam preoccupied with the writhing snake. The snake's eye turned back in response to God's wild laughter, while Eve weeps – or maybe she is laughing too and it is only Adam who doesn't have a sense of humour. Adam has an apple in his cheek. He's eaten it whole, but there's more humour in a pineapple. His toes touch Eve's heel as Adam rubs his eyes. Maybe they are all laughing at God's joke, or the joke of God who almost falls from the cloud with his punchline.

From bull, to god, to the mourning stationery, at last!

The mourning stationery, it says, came out of the Victorian age, or maybe before. The mourning stationery edged with black borders, associated with the death of a spouse. I try not to think of that as I push my nose to the mourning veils, fans, pins of steel, handkerchiefs, purses, jet bead necklaces. Often, strands of the deceased's hair was woven into rings and broaches, it says; accessories also include tear bottles and golf balls. There's an advert for Deep Mourning Costumes: *costumes made expressly for unexpected mourning ready for immediate wear, at moderate prices. Dresses made to order at the shortest notice.* There are images of love letters bound in red ribbon alongside the mourning letters in bundles bound in black ribbon. Silk bookmarks also commemorate the dead. Now it's all orange sunsets, single roses, folded hands, angels with upturned eyes and Jesus in his best daywear waiting at the gates of paradise.

The depth of black, edging the mourning stationery, corresponds to the depth of mourning; the width and tone, it says, *lessens as the mourning lightens*. The assumption that it does, and what happens if the reverse is true? Do you end up with a white square the size of a postage stamp to write on? *Originally the borders were 3/8 to 1/2 of an inch, announcing "deepest retirement." A 1/4-inch border was later deemed sufficient for deepest mourning. 3/16 to 1/32 of an inch were suitable widths for a second mourning.* It did not state the suitable width for the loss of a whole family, several children, a whole nation, or beloved pets.

There are books of stamps in the cabinet besides the mourning stationery. National bereavement stamps with added black borders, like the stamps that were issued when Lenin died, with borders that were black and red. Mourning stamps with doves and pale orange roses. Later when I read about mourning stamps I find what are called *Operation Iraq stamps,* with pictures of Abu Ghraib. The amount will be given in $, so the stamps give the impression that they were pressed to the tongues, forefingers and envelopes of the American people.

The now-iconic images reduced to tiny sets for sale beside the *Darfur Genocide* and collector's stamps of *Winnie the Pooh*.

I have no idea what kind of stamp you used on the letter. Will most likely never see the envelope that was taken away. It was not Christmas; there was no occasion as far as I know; no commemoration stamps were at the time in issue. Nothing more than the Queen's head. I wonder if she was perfectly placed in the right-hand corner, all present and correct, the Queen upright with no fear of blood rushing to her head. I like to place the Queen on her head. It's my only revenge. There's no added charge or fine for putting Her Majesty at a jaunty angle; that can happen when I'm in a rush. Imagine our heads replicated like that, held, the back of your head licked by so many types and sizes of tongues, the stink and sweetness of strangers' breath.

In the case of your letter the postmark, we'll say, was blurred, as is so often the case – a stroke of luck – not that you gave any pretence that you were new in town, from another city; the threat was that you were and are on the doorstep. In this case there was no need for the human error or the blur of whatever machine marks the letters, a broken circle, the suggestion of a raft floating on a wave or two. The postmark gave nothing extra away.

AM–2007–ff

Modern postmarks, or so I read, *are often applied simultaneously with the cancellation or "killer" that marks the postage stamps as having been used. A killer and postmark form a continuous design. Postmarks for ships and rail delivery are different. Hawaiian post once had a postmark in the form of a surfboard for covers that travelled this way.*

I once had a post office kit given to me for Christmas: *Children's Mail*. Everything needed to play postmistress. Fifty sheets of paper, twenty envelopes, twenty postcards, two wooden stamps, one inkpad, one sponge, no water provided, one hundred postage stamps of all colours and from a range of countries. Pop-up counter. It even had a small model post office with traditional stone features, an exterior staircase, an outside toilet, post office paraphernalia, licences and letters, a post office sign, a cat and flower boxes. My brother was always the customer.

~

At the museum there's a small post office that until today I had forgotten all about. Find myself running outside into the museum grounds to find it, to greet it with the smile I would normally reserve for a loved one. It is something I have passed many times, and I've never paid attention to the tiny post office that now pulls me outside to search the small map. Number thirteen; lucky for me that the post office has been relocated from its original home to settle beside the museum bakery, the smell of freshly baked tin loaves and tea-bread, the baker telling me that everything is made to her own recipe. Opposite there's a tailor's shop and a little way to the left a general stores.

The post office measures 5.05 metres long by 2.9 metres wide. Each brick, years back, had been numbered and moved from its original site many miles from here. It has two windows. The one on the left looks into the private part of the shop, where there's a small unlit fire, a radio, teapot, a photograph of the postmaster at the door to the post office in its original setting. The postman's wife Hannah Griffiths was the postmistress. Mr Griffiths worked in the Lamb Inn, the public house just opposite. If someone called at the post office while Hannah was serving at the inn, customers could press a small button that activated a bell behind the bar – not dissimilar to the panic alarm button that had been under our TV.

The post office has a mat inside, faded from the number of people who have stood there waiting for stamps. The mat reads *Drink Typhoo Tea*. Hannah was obviously partial to her brew. The date on the wall is 6th December, no year specified. There's another photograph of Mr G; Hannah is missing. Maybe Hannah snapped the photograph. Mr G is happy and proud of his work. He's standing in the post office, sorting mail or giving the impression that he is. In the other photograph, where he stands outside the post office in its original location, it looks as if it is up high on a hill. There's a small wall to the right of the building and an expanse of sky and light. Mr G is smiling and holding a cigarette between his teeth. His pose is rather awkward, despite the boyish openness of his smile. Wide grin, eyes bright, almost deranged, caught by Hannah. The cigarette is not yet burnt down, if indeed it is lit at all. He holds himself straight, his right side turned toward us, his right arm rigid and his hand curled at the end of his ill-fitting suit the way a child might pose for a school photograph. His leg, almost unable to keep up with his torso, which arches back a little in its attempt to look upright and ready beside his post box – a bleak-looking box with no writing and no postal times and no allure that encourages you to leave the letters to its care. There's a pamphlet pinned to the wall with information about dried eggs. A poster reading *Dig for Victory*. A second poster reads, *You never know who's listening! Careless talk costs lives*.

The clock has stopped at two minutes to twelve – midday or midnight? The post office has the faint odour of an outside toilet – it may be dampness from the dark chocolate walls rather than urine, but it causes me to consider where Mr G, and Hannah could relieve themselves in this small building. Most likely they'd nip over to The Lamb. The empty grate in Hannah's small room at the back makes me want to go get some coal for the fire.

Did Hannah ever burn the odd letter, the odd undecipherable mail, deceased, undelivered post? What happened to all the dead letters? Did anyone ever threaten Hannah via Royal Mail?

The backs of shops never lose their sense of trespass. Even here at the museum we are not allowed into this old post office, and so I am left to peer through the windows over a half-opened stable door like an old horse that's been locked out, arse end out. The back rooms I remember as a child: the wool shop, Mary and Derek the grocers, my friend's aunt's wallpaper shop, Vivien's. People who formed tiny corner shops at the front of their terraced houses. If you got invited out back, into the private room, it made you feel chosen. That side of the counter, that side of selling, that view of customers' change and wants.

There's a small booklet at the post office left out near the doorway on a bit of string. It has information on how they moved the building from its original site. Ithel, the curator, writes that it took his team a week to mark out the post office and dismantle it from its original site hundreds of miles away, and about four weeks to rebuild it in its new home in the museum grounds. Each of the stones – or in this case bricks – had to be numbered. Two lines run at right angles to each other, pulled through the building. Each dimension is then recorded off these lines. Any stone larger than a pebble is given a letter and a number, an A-to-Z system. The post office bound with a cross of taut string gives it the appearance of a giant parcel, with lettered bricks forming an address. The buildings have to be excavated, Ithel writes, rather than demolished. Often because there are things hidden beneath or inside the buildings that may be of value. There are two classes of finds recovered: those deliberately placed there, and those lost or thrown into the foundations as rubbish. The first class includes all sorts of objects with magical or protective powers, like horse's skulls, shoes – which in particular were used as fertility symbols: babies' shoes laid in pairs inside chimney breasts and loft space, under floorboards. There are those who believe the buildings should look pristine, that that would make the public believe that it had always been here, or at least maintain the illusion that it had. When people visit the buildings here it is the little things that they remember, he says. Like poking their fingers into a hole which exposes the layers of the house or building, a fire in the hearth.

It would trouble me as a child, when we'd decorate, seeing the vulnerability of the house exposed beneath torn paper, hacked plaster. I look at the numbered bricks in the picture, lettered, circled. I remember the letter at the back of my notebook, a copy of your words that I have with me. When I peep at your letter, trying not to read it too carefully, I see that I have ringed this copy and numbered words, circled parts of sentences. If I don't take in the meaning it almost looks like a pretty letter now, like a side of a building waiting to be moved. Details are a must, Ithel says in his write-up: *When moving a building like this post office, details are everything, like the protection of a house, the number of post boxes.* I look closer at the photograph of Mr G. He is smiling again in this other image. No one ever thought of donating a post office – their home, their every day together – to a museum when Mr G was alive. *Perish the thought*, they might have said. Mr G in his best suit, starched collar and neat tie has a look of Beckett about him. Not because of the attire, more because of his hair and bone structure, and less because of his smile; Beckett rarely smiled as much as Mr G does – in photographs, at least.

There is a drawing Ithel made in the book, a wooden counter box he so carefully drew, a small hole for the mail. The attention Ithel has given to this drawing, to the detail of the keyhole, touches me. There's a faint copy of a telegram. Only the word, *Regret,* is visible; during the war this small post office had doubled as a centre for information – or so the article reads: *If the Invaders Come Keep Watch.* In light of my writing to you that makes me smile. *Keep watch,* it says. *Do not give your enemy anything. Hide your food and your bicycles. Hide your maps. Keep your pecker up.* Ithel also explains in the booklet that there was a competition created to coincide with the post office opening at the museum in May 1992. The challenge: *Produce a presentation on the theme of My Post Office. Focusing on the vital role it plays at the heart of every community. Post a little happiness,* the caption reads. There's a picture of the fire lit up – Hannah's side. Not a small fire in the grate but a roaring inviting fire, plenty of coal and wood layered up. The fire lit at last. No business. A quiet whiff, as father would say; a stillness, a moment's rest as if Hannah had just popped over to The Lamb, the fire, the promise of return. If only I could reach the small button that would call her back to me. Still, I'll forget to ask who is responsible now for banking up and keeping good the fire here at the museum, who has the job of collecting the wood, chopping it, keeping it dry, twisting the paper between, sugar for the coals, stoking – Hannah's fire, Hannah's home, the post, habits of a lifetime.

As I peer into the post office, people pass. They comment on the parcel that's on the scales, tied with string, a perfect knot almost as pretty as a rosebud, a seal of red wax. It makes me want to know what's inside, if anything at all; if it's pretence or a leftover parcel that Hannah never delivered. It makes me want to jump the stable door and shake the parcel, unwrap it. Tell Hannah and Mr G of the parcels I'll later find being sold online with the bundles of Victorian love letters alongside the three brown parcels that belonged to Sherlock Holmes, the fiction, the destination, both man and address, and what of the contents? At £4 for 3 parcels, it's hard to imagine there is anything authentic about them or they'd surely cost more. Maybe letters; letters to Sherlock walled up inside a parcel. The delicious idea of owning parcels that you must or will never open. Neither did Sherlock open them; despite the clues, it is true to say, the parcels never arrived.

When I can get back to the stable door I notice that on the post office shelf there's a Dr Barnardo's house; I was only writing about them the other day. I cannot remember who owned them or why I was writing about them. The collection boxes, that is. The collection boxes that were in the shape of a house; the chapel women carried them. The small gold houses, more like cottages. My mother wasn't a chapel woman so we only got to hold the boxes for as long as it took to make a donation. Each week Mr Fish would call on his wife's behalf. His wife was a chapel woman. Mr Fish carrying the house, shaking the box. I believe there was a real Barnardo's house in town. It didn't have trees on the side, nor plants; it looked nothing like the small gold collection box. People didn't talk to the Barnardo's kids, because they were Barnardo's kids, but they collected well.

If you move to the left-hand window of the post office you can get a better view, although there's not a letter in sight. They've forgotten the obvious. They've an old radio where Hannah would listen to the golden oldies or the shipping forecast while she sorted out the mail. The repetition of the shop bell in the distance as people pass in and out, reminding me of that film, *It's a Wonderful Life*. Every time the bell rang an angel got their wings. A Chinese woman now claims the post office for seconds. – I like this post office, she says. She touches the wall of the post office as if it is a pet. A bell ringing each time a letter is delivered. – Let's go, the American man tells the Chinese woman as he takes her picture. I am guarding the post office, I want to say. With my pen and my position at the stable door, on the bench, to and fro. I'm sitting here and can see that people are fond of their post offices. Most people stop at the post office and say things like, – At least this one is open, even if they closed most of the real ones; or, – I'd like one of these at the bottom of the garden. Some are silent in front of the tiny post office. Even the robins visit, red-breasted like the box. It's a Christmas scene, me sitting here, already it's midwinter, like the photograph I'll find of the post office covered in snow, the red telephone box beside it, glowing in the half-light. Footprints in the snow, undecided, change direction. The robin just flown from the branches is missing but its presence is still felt. Soon it will be the same date as on display: December 6th. The year that Mr Griffiths died, I was just two years old and knew nothing of him. The bench is not memorialised to him or anyone else. People read the information written about the post office as if they were reading a gravestone. Some laugh. Some whisper the words to one another and stand very close together, arms touching as they read: *Mrs Hannah Griffiths would deliver mail by bicycle to the surrounding farms and cottages. A journey of some eight miles which she undertook each morning before starting work in the Lamb Inn. The post office is at the centre of communication. Mr Griffiths died in 1962.* No one mentions the death of Mrs Griffiths. There is no freestanding post box; the bicycle, photographed in front of the building, is now missing.

I like to think that Hannah Griffiths did not follow Mr G in 1962. That the last parcels unposted remain in remembrance of him. That, in grief and not wanting to resort to mourning stationery, Hannah took her postmistress bicycle out that day and was never seen again. That she rode in a straight line, as straight as lines can be when lines and roads and grief cause us to wobble. She rode quietly to a place where there were only expanses of skies, unpeopled fields, no more than a few gentle cows, no letterboxes – for a time at least, nothing red to remind her. Hannah refrained from using the bell both as a mark of respect and because she knew that the bell would not bring back Mr G, nor give him the wings he so deserved. They were beyond this fiction.

The postman's story – the postman who loves Elvis

I've been a postman for many years and it was only because I was going to talk to you today about my work that I started reading up about the history of it. That the post didn't begin until the fifteenth century when people, if they were well-off, sent letters via servants. Poorer people relied on travellers to carry messages. Churches and universities sent regular messages and the Royals had their own couriers. They carried the messages in bags embroidered with the royal arms. Later on, wooden posts, ten to twenty miles apart, were set up between innkeepers who would make sure the messengers had fresh horses. Charges were later introduced that depended on the miles the mail was sent. Now it's calculated by weight and size, but once people were charged for the number of sheets of paper they used, so it was common for people to write letters from top to bottom and then turn the page horizontally and begin the next part of the letter on top of the writing beneath.

Back in the old days, soldiers became postmen when they left the army. That's historically how people got into delivering the mail. Well, I knew that before, that quotas of the people employed were ex-servicemen. It's also quite romantic, the idea of letters coming all the way from the trenches and the outposts, how far letters would travel and how they got through what seemed like impossible remoteness and circumstances. I don't really write letters any more. We used to, back in the old days, but now it's more emailing, Christmas cards, birthday cards, and special days. That's all I personally do. Every Christmas from the post office, all the posties get fifty stamped envelopes that they can use to send letters for free. I hardly use them. I remember when we were young, when we then lived abroad, we used to have what we called letter friends, through school maybe. Letter friends in Denmark, I think it was. First eleven years of school – I studied in eight, nine different schools – my father was a policeman and it isn't like it is here, we moved around a lot because of his job and I was always away from home and so I remember we would write letters a lot, to keep contact with friends. When I met my wife, I think in the first two years she got over three hundred letters from me, I wrote her all the time. That's what we did, and I came across the letters some time ago and she's got bundles of them. It's funny; when you are apart you write them all the time, and then when you live together you don't so much, if at all; but I think if you can still do that it's lovely, because you can put down what you cannot say face to face. My wife is very artistic and likes designing things, she used to sit down and write letters to me. If I am honest she still does, even though we live together.

Despite all the complaints we get about the post office – things have changed so much these days and the service is not like it was – there's still that romantic view of the post itself.

When I first started, it was run in a very military kind of way, run with the same sort of discipline. For example, if you were working on the sorting, you were allowed to sit down only for periods and had to stand up for the rest of the time. You'd have to ask permission to go to the toilet. You had two uniforms, your summer and your winter outfits, and you always looked smart. There was respect in the job then. I can't believe I'm talking about the old days with such rosy eyes. Going back ten, twelve years ago, things were so different, like the times when we still had canvas bags – the ones probably made by prisoners. Each depot had special machines that would clean all the bags, that was all done on site at what was called the bag centre. You had people turning out the bags to make sure there were no letters stuck inside. This was done weekly. Imagine how many sacks there were and how filthy they'd get.

The parcel centre used to be a place of amazement to me. All

242

these chutes, which looked like water chutes, held and moved all the parcels along. That was where all the old men worked, and there were so many parcels piled high that you'd look around the huge room and you wouldn't see anyone and you'd think you were there alone with all these parcels everywhere and then a little head would pop up from between the piles – it was comical. And on a Thursday, one of the bosses would run a little fruit shop. He'd have piles of bananas, tangerines, apples and the like, and when you'd go in to collect your wages in a packet, he would sell you your fruit for the week. Now you are under pressure all the time to meet targets. But back in the old days everyone would have time for you and would want to stop you and talk to you. We only used to deliver first and second-class mail; now we are expected to deliver all sorts of mail, so much more junk and advertising. I was a telegram boy for a while; now all that is gone. You don't get the letters from the Queen any more like you used to.

At the place where I work we have special vans and we have to share them between us. I work in a delivery office as well. The mail comes in and is sorted manually in the main office into different divisions. We do this together. There are different aisles where you sit down and there are post boxes for each postman. When the mail comes in everyone sits down and sorts the boxes. Each postie then takes their own box and goes to their desk. When you go on your desk there are little spaces for each house. Some streets are consecutive, some odds and evens, but basically every house is represented by a small gap, and each letter goes in there, if there is post for that house. There are now new machines that they are bringing in, and the machine will soon replace manual sorting. In the future the bundles of post will come ready for the postie to deliver. They are already doing this in some European countries – in Holland, for example. People here are already on one-day contracts.

I began the job when a family friend – he was a manager in a central post office – suggested I give it a try; and I like being outdoors. I never liked working indoors. And when you get into it, it is the type of job that you either love or you don't. Three days training and then I was out there on my own, delivering the mail. It is really demanding. There are consequences to all that walking around and you don't always realise how much the walking around and carrying those bags wears you out. You have the typical postman's knee, shoulder, back and ankle injuries. But it is really good fun. It's the type of job ... well, I was talking to one of my ex-colleagues, he is ninety-five, and I couldn't do it, he said, an office job, I couldn't. That kind of person gets into the job and they stick with it. It's a great job. You know, four o'clock in the morning, you drive along the empty streets and then you get into the delivery office and it's like a circus. You walk in and it's a really, really lively atmosphere. You know everyone, and it is surprising how much people tell you so that in the end you know everything about the families you deliver to ... There are many funny stories ...

When you walk into some front gardens and you don't see anyone, you think that nobody is home, but they are watching you, they know. For example, you walk in and as soon as you come to the letterbox they'll fling open the door. Lonely people. Older people usually. There are places where you see the same people do the same thing at the same time every day; like where I park outside number 14. Each day there is an old lady, she sits in the window and reads. I park my van and when I approach, the dog goes nuts at the door. The woman with the dog, she will lean over her TV and always look out of the window; when she sees me she waves, and then sometimes she carries on watching TV or reading for a short while as if she is pretending she is not in a rush to come and talk to me. Mostly she will see me and take the dog out immediately. Follow me up the road. She does the same thing each day. You get to know people and their patterns. If you are off for a while they always ask people – where is our postman? You really get attached to people's lives.

I was thinking the other day about our relationship with the windows in our home and how this changes depending on our mood or what's happened or not happening. For instance, if people are feeling quite dreamy or down maybe, or missing someone, they might pull a chair to the window more than usual, with their eyes staring out across the road, or they might actually stand in the window for ages. Especially when people are grief-stricken, they spend a lot more time at the window.

Sometimes you can feel bad when you deliver the mail. Well, it can feel awkward because you know what is coming before they do, you know that there are things coming for people. You can work things out from the postcodes: official things, personal things. Yes, it's very intimate. You can tell by the way they box things and by the markings and where things have come from. I know things, for example, things that people's neighbours wouldn't know. Like if you were getting a final notice from somewhere. I am just your postman but I would know for example if you two were getting divorced. I would know from the paperwork and where it came from. You can tell for instance when people's children come back home to live again. There are all these stories. If you worked your way down the whole street I could tell you about what is going on in most of the houses. Without even trying you get into people's lives through these objects and packages we carry. And some of the things we deliver are ridiculous. We get lots of students whose family send them food from various countries, they send things like sausage, or fish, and the packets stink. And we also get insects being delivered to people who keep reptiles and have to feed them with live creatures and you can hear things moving inside the packets. We have such contrasts in one delivery. Like this morning: I had a bouquet of flowers in a box, a wrapped-up tyre, and a golf stick bound in brown paper – the different shapes. There are weight restrictions, yes, but whatever is carriable we usually deliver.

Things now have to go through the machines that read the letters, and if they are bulky sometimes, or badly wrapped, they get torn. If something has been damaged, hasn't been packaged properly or has come unwrapped it has to be shown to a manager. If there is writing on the outside of the package or letters, something rude or obscene, with some swearing or scribble on it, then I can endorse it, but I have to show it to a senior person. If I show it to them the postie is safe, so if it is ripped or has writing on it then the people know it is not us who did it. Also your fingertips get very sensitive so that you know what is inside things. You also know if they get naughty things. Magazines. The amount of stuff that comes through, sometimes pornographic, substances, weird objects and images. There was one occasion where a man had sent a postcard of his girlfriend, something he'd made himself, a photograph of his girlfriend with no clothes on; they'd obviously split up, and he had written on the back that he was sending it to her to let her know that he'd circulated it to all her friends. The I.B., the Investigation Bureau at the depot, has to deal with things like that and they had to go around to the woman and explain what had happened. You have a lot of stuff sometimes coming from places like *Leather Weekly* or *Anne Summers*, you can imagine. It's kind of funny. If sometimes it hasn't been packed very well and it's broken open, the office has to put it into a clear plastic bag with an apology and you then have to deliver it. Once I had to hand over a vibrator in this see-through bag to a young woman, it was really embarrassing.

The other thing that is common is that some women like to open the door not wearing anything at all. Unless it is a new postman who is not used to it we don't take a lot of notice; it's just part of the job. One woman – well, the daughter lives with her mother, and the daughter, nineteen or twenty, she opens the door in French knickers and there she is leaning against the door, going, – Morning, postie, how are you… Morning … in a very suggestive voice. You just have to laugh. Oh, and there was a woman I knew who lived at number 38 and I delivered to that house for twelve, thirteen months and she never answered the door with clothes on. Well, she had pants probably, but the top of the door was glass, frosted glass and as she would lean her head around the door, she would press her chest to the glass so I could see. Window cleaners would have the same thing happen. Some houses are a bit low so when you walk down into the garden there they are, in the bedroom waiting for you to reach the same level as the window and the window is open. Some people have very monotone lives.

You also get really funny insults sometimes from the public, like when someone is no longer at an address that you keep delivering mail to, and I have had letters back where the new occupant living at the address has written things like: *He's fucking dead!* You laugh but you have to take it to the manager. You have to say, – Look, there is writing on this but I didn't write it, it came like that. The other thing you get in all the junk mail is things that promise people money that say things like … *You are the last three to win £50,000,* yet you know that in your hand you have hundreds of envelopes and letters saying the same thing.

We do get warnings if there is a bomb threat. It means that instead of looking forward to the post as you always had, you can start to dread it. There was one place targeted recently by a letter bomb. A women working in the post room was injured when she opened it. There is standard procedure to follow, things to watch out for: like if a letter or packet is too heavy for the box or if it smells of marzipan, or feels greasy ... or is ticking! That's a good sign... If there are any doubts the bomb squad come down. In the old days there might be day-trips to the depot and if they found something suspicious they'd place a polystyrene box over it – as if that would take care of it. All this going on while the old ladies who were still on their tour were asking inane questions about what different sections of the post office did, and then the bomb squad would come and get us all out, open up the parcel and find it was just a cake or something!

Sometimes we get mail we can't deliver, where someone might just write Stephen Jones and the name of the town. When we get those it's hard because you know you can't find them. If we had a letter for example to Mrs Nettleby and the name of the town, we wouldn't immediately send that off to Belfast where all the unsent letters go, we would try and work it out, ask other postmen; people get to know their houses and sometimes between us we can work it out. For example this morning we had such a letter and the other postie couldn't work it out or remember, it had just a name on it. And he showed it to me and I said, – Well, that's easy, that's just the last house on the corner, cos I would know if it is my patch. Once we'd spend a lot more time trying to match the stray letters with people but now we are told more often to just kill those letters off. When we can't trace the person, that's what we call the letters, kill-off letters. We kill them off. What happens is, when we get letters refused or letters that cannot be delivered because someone has gone away, or there is no forwarding or return address, whatever the reason, they all end up in Belfast in the Dead Letters office, letters from all over Britain. There they have the job of opening the letters up and looking for clues, even the letters marked private and confidential. All the undelivered letters are opened there and they try and find an address. I don't know what the

248

law is but I think if there is no return address inside then they have to keep the letter for two years and then they have to burn it. What a great job that must be, reading all the letters. But it's strange and sad to think of them burning. Like in the book by the guy who wrote *Moby Dick*. Do you know that? There's a story he wrote called Bartleby and at the end Bartleby ends up working in the Office of Lost Letters. I had scribbled that down to mention it to you today. *Dead letters!* It says ... *continually handling these dead letters, and assorting them for the flames? For by the cartload they are annually burned ... On errands of life, these letters speed to death.*

Yeah, and at Christmas time we get all the Santa mail. Children write to Santa, about what they want for Christmas. I don't know where all that goes, there must be a department for it. And the Santa mail gets collected there and Santa writes back to them.

Occasionally you get some oddball stories of someone abusing their job, but it's rare. I did remember a story someone told me once: she said that she had a boyfriend who was a postman and when he couldn't be bothered working all morning, he'd dump the mail in skips or in tree hollows. She said that when he told her this she couldn't go out with him any more as it changed how she thought about him, changed everything. It doesn't happen often. As soon as the post is missing there is a private investigation bureau that tracks the person. They are like the equivalent of the police; they have the same powers of arrest and can strip your car and search your home. Each post depot has an I.B. room upstairs, an interview room with tape recorders where if they are suspicious, they can interview you and conduct an investigation on the spot. Where we work in the sorting rooms, above, there's a walkway made up of black windows that we can't see into but the I.B. above are walking around keeping an eye on us all; there are cameras everywhere too and sometimes they'll have men working alongside you as plants, they'll pass wads of money or open parcels through the machines to see if anyone will take anything. There was someone once who used to do his deliveries really fast. He'd been working in the job for ten years or more. The bosses used to hold him up as an example as he'd work so much quicker than the rest of us. In the end someone reported him and the I.B. raided the house of the guy, and when they did they couldn't get into his house for mail. He had been collecting it up for two years or so and been selling all the birthday presents and items he'd found in the post on E-bay. Posties who like their job, that isn't something they'd ever do: throwing the mail, or stealing it away … no. As I said, over time you get to know people. You get fond of people. You also get to know where the dogs are too and when not to put your fingers through the door.

Of course most postmen have to deal with dangerous dogs. Oh yes, that is part of a postman's job. You have a walk log you are supposed to keep updated – to tell other postmen where the dangerous dogs are. Often the logs aren't kept up. I was bitten once around the ankles by a small dog. On one of the council estates one of my friend's was bitten by a Rottweiler; it was funny in one sense because the dog bit his buttocks. If you are bitten you have to take a picture as well as fill in forms for the records. You have to sit down with a manager and you have to go through pages of reports, go to the doctor to get a jab or whatever. In my case I was bitten by a Jack Russell. I had to go through all that palaver and take a picture. My friend was trying to take a picture in the toilet and he couldn't take the picture of his buttock at the right angle, so when he went home he had to get his mother to take it for him. The dogs, it's like they almost get trained so that when the postman comes …

I learned my lesson after that. I have been working with the Romani for a long time now. They still call them the Gypsies round here, and years back no one would deliver to the camp. There's a permanent one nearby. Originally what they used to do was just drive by the camp and fling the mail out and then rush off again and no one would go in there. Then the Gypsies went to the travellers' representative and complained that they wanted their mail delivered like everyone else's. And so about eighteen years ago I agreed to go in and build up some friendships with people, as that's how I'd always approached the job. The first day they gave me a map of all the different caravan numbers but when you get inside the way it's laid out is quite confusing: all the numbers are all over the place. At first people were very suspicious and it took a week or so before someone said, – You all right, Postie! And then within a couple of weeks I had gained people's trust. There are around seventy or eighty dogs in there, some tied up and some running all over, some in coops like rabbit hutches, and some of it I found upsetting because I am a real big animal lover and some of the dogs were really mean and I said to myself, how am I going to cope with this? So I started buying chews for the dogs. They'd come charging out at me snarling and then I'd throw them a chew, and they'd settle right down and over the years I was able to go into parts of the camp that even some of the people who lived there wouldn't go to. Sometimes I'd be stroking the dogs, huge things, and someone would say, – What are you doing, he'll rip you to pieces … but I'd feed them and they'd calm down. I have got so used to it now. I always go round there with big bags of dog food, *Baker's Complete*, and the dogs all come out, and the kids sometimes come out and they follow me around asking for the meat to feed the dogs. One kid came out shouting at me, – Oi! … Give us some meat … And I said to him, – What's the magic word? and he just stood there looking at me and you could see his mind ticking over and he said, – Abracadabra. And you can't argue with that, can you; that's great.

Sometimes I've gone back and seen dogs I've been feeding only the day before, just stretched out dead in the road. I do find that bit hard. You get attached to some of them. The people too, they have been good to me, and they've done me lots of favours. The first time, when someone I knew died at the camp, the others were asking me to go pay my respects and I didn't know what the protocol was so I didn't, but when another guy died, he was one of the main men there, I decided I should do the right thing. I knew by then what was expected. He was always very good to me, always gave me a big Christmas tip and looked after me if I needed anything. Anyway, when he died, they asked me to go into his caravan to see him. Inside they had decorated the whole place with white silk and he was lying there on a white bed and I had to sit in the caravan on my own with him. When I came out one of the women said to me, – Did you touch him? – No, No, I told her, I didn't touch a thing in there. And she said, – You should have cos he's still warm!

Quite often I have to read out the letters for people at the camp as some of them can't read. At first it took me a while to get used to that, grown men asking you to read with them, and sometimes people get warrants for their arrest, or some of the women there have been done for shoplifting, that's hard, but they usually laugh and say, – Is that all ... that's okay then! Some of the young people get love letters, saying things like I want to marry you. Sometimes the spelling is a bit dodgy and you have to make up words you think would fit, or carry on the sentiment...

People outside are so narrow-minded about the camp but the people who live there are always good to me. It's away from the camp in your day-to-day work that you meet your share of weirdos. Most of them are locals so you get to know people. One lady on our round is a bouncer, she never likes being woken up in the morning. She's a real big strong woman. There's a safe point. You get to know where to leave the mail and who to leave alone.

People have different patterns, like people who take drugs regularly and are up most of the night, or people who work nights.

I have never been verbally threatened or hit or anything like that but now I think about it, there are a few stories about threats I've received. Well, nothing violent, more just strange and worrying incidents. It's not always clear-cut but when they happened these things made me quite concerned. One of them is still ongoing. For example, there was a woman who wrote to me once, that felt quite threatening as I didn't know her at all apart from the fact I delivered her mail, and she must have taken a shine to me. She wrote out of the blue saying that she was postponing her wedding because she wanted to be with me. Someone else gave the letter to me. A friend of hers, I guess, came running down the road one day when I was delivering and said she'd been asked to pass a message on to me, and there was this letter with my name on it. I was really concerned that if anything ever happened, I mean if she accused me of something… I gave all the letters she started sending me to my colleague in work, because I wanted someone to have proof, just in case. I am not being disrespectful, I know I am a big bloke and can look after myself, but it did frighten the life out of me at the time, and I still worry about seeing her because I hadn't done anything. I had to go around and knock on her door – which in hindsight was silly as I was alone and she could have done anything, but I wanted to tell her it was ridiculous…

Then there was another woman who was working in a supermarket where I had to deliver mail each day and she looked all glum, and being friendly I said, – Oh, come on, what's wrong? At the time they were playing music in the store, and at that moment it was a song called *Love Lifts Us Up Where We Belong*, and I made some comment about the nice song and said, – Come on, you should be happy, you've got good music on… And then the next day she turned up at the beginning of my delivery, at the sorting office, and I said to her, – What are you doing here. And she said, – Well, you know, what you said about the music yesterday, *Up Where We Belong*... You obviously meant me and you, didn't you? – No, I said, you've got the wrong end of the stick. But after that she sent quite a few letters to me. One was like an essay. That was quite scary. She wrote about six or seven pages about me and her and how we were meant to be together... Again, I covered myself by giving the letters to my colleague by asking him to keep them. I was scared when the woman wrote those letters to me and showed up at the depot; I thought she was capable of anything at the time, and I still look out for her now, worry I might see her again, say the wrong thing. Sometimes you are quite vulnerable, as part of your job is to try and be friendly, to get around, to try and make things easier, and sometimes people invite you in, ask you to do something, help move something or whatever, and sometimes the places are quite remote. And it's hard to judge with people, it can go either way...

More recently, again in a supermarket, there was this guy, a security guard working on the door – and I do like Elvis, I'm a big fan – the first couple of days I was delivering there. It was raining and I had my collar up and I had my hair brushed back and he was looking at me and he had a little smirk on his face, and I did get a bit worried about him and the way he was behaving when he saw me. Anyway, I was coming out of the supermarket one day after my delivery there, and he came over to me and started talking to me saying, – Thank you very much, but in an Elvis voice. Then he asked if I liked Elvis and I told him, – Yeah, I do. Trying at the same time to leave the store, saying that I was in a rush... But then we got talking and having a laugh and a joke and I thought; well he seems okay, there's no malice, so we'd chat. When I went back to do my usual delivery over the next few days, to be honest he seemed quite sensible, genuine. If there is one thing I hate it's Elvis impersonators, all those people walking around in all sorts of costumes; I think it's derogatory to the man and the Elvis world. To begin with, he was just interested in the history and the music I had. Then he invited me to go and look over his Elvis record collection and I said I didn't mind because I have a lot of things I've collected over the years, and at auctions, and I thought I could see what he had.

He lives in a block of flats and when I got there I rang the buzzer; he was talking as Elvis through the intercom and then he started singing Elvis songs. He came bounding down to let me in and from then on in it got very weird. At the time, when I'd met him in the store and we'd been talking about what Elvis things we had, I'd felt a bit sorry for him because he obviously wasn't paid a lot and couldn't afford much. So I'd told him I had a couple of books, duplicates, one that was worth quite a bit; I'd taken it in for him and said he could have it. I told him it was a collector's item. When I went up to his flat, I saw that he had cut up the book and spread the pictures all over the walls. After that he started phoning me at home, and his phone calls would go on for two hours. You could go off and do other things and come back and he'd still be talking. I tried all ways to get rid of him but he kept on ringing. Then he began saying that he was a better Elvis fan than me, getting very competitive, not that I cared, but he obviously did. And then he'd phone up and leave messages on the answerphone, talking again in an Elvis voice or he'd sing to me over the phone. In the end he was playing me things he'd recorded. Then it became too much. I think there's always an element of Elvis fans that are not quite right. The press especially always portray the fans who are extreme, like the guy who this Christmas was making some toast, heard the smoke alarm go off, went back to the kitchen pulled out the burnt bread and said that on it was the face of Elvis…

Anyway, I think this guy is a little in that mould. He kept saying he wanted to see my collection of Elvis memorabilia and

I kept making excuses and in the end gave in because he kept on and on … I thought, I'll just do it, just the once – then that'll be that. I have a buckle and some trousers that Elvis wore on stage, things like that, and before he came around I got them out, the belt, the buckle. When he turned up he began singing one of Elvis's songs, *Hurt*, several renditions of it in a really loud voice; and at the time the windows were open, it was a nice day, and I was worried that the neighbours would think it was me singing. After that he then took out a loan, which must have almost bankrupted him, to go to Graceland. And when he was there he filmed the whole thing. Made me copies of the twelve DVDs he took and posted it all through my door. When I played them I realised that he had narrated the whole twelve films to me. He kept talking to me directly on the film, he kept saying things like, – I bet you wish you were here, don't you … bet you do. Before he left for the trip he filmed himself in the mirror, talking to me, he kept using my name, saying, – I'm off now, to Graceland. He also said that he'd written my name on the wall at Graceland, next to his, and he filmed everything, even when he was walking he filmed all the time, the ground, he never cut off the filming, he just filmed all the time while talking to me. And don't get me wrong, I love Elvis and I'll watch anything of his, about him, or with him in it, but when it is all aimed at you and someone keeps saying, I'm here and you're not … then it got … Well, it is quite a weird situation.

He still calls but only now and again, and I make excuses that I'm busy. He also keeps saying that he wants to come to my house again. And he recently threatened to get someone to burgle my house, for the memorabilia. He said he had friends that could break in and … he's said this a couple of times and sometimes the things he says are worrying … It's hard to know, but sometimes I do wonder if he'll just turn up at my house. I often hope he just won't remember the way.

Day Pages – Spain

It'll come around quickly enough. That's what people say about an occasion, an event on its way, how it scares you. Sunday: evening of the bullfight. It arrives well enough and here we are already watching people photograph the matadors. Realising later that these older, fatter men in their yellow costumes – men more solid than fat – are not in fact matadors but the picadors on the way to the bullring. I come to learn these simple enough facts over time; mostly this morning, as we took a guided tour, something we have not done in twenty years of visits here.

This time we broke our own rule. I persuaded En. I hold up my hand to it. I was floundering at the time, imagining an hour round the ring would give me more of an idea, I N-F O R M A T I O N, more stalling. Either way, I learned the names of a few things, like the name of the fence that runs around the ring of sand, the barrera. Inside the barrera is the circular wooden corridor, or callejon, which fronts the first row of seats; seats where we'll find ourselves later. The callejon, where the picadors wait their turn between acts. Three acts beginning with the picadors. That's what I learned.

We'll have trouble later finding our seats on the evening of the corrida: it all looks the same. Enter through the big iron gates and it's elaborate as you'd expect, it's tiled with the names of every famous matador who was carried through at the end of a fight. To be carried through the gates on the shoulders of your fellow matadors is the highest accolade, or so the guide said. We'll look at the tiled names and the pictures of the matadors who died and then, once inside, we'll literally go round in circles.

First act to come, we'll make our way round and around the dark outer corridors. There they'll be, the horses, already dressed in their padding and blindfolds, dressed up like chess pieces, or like those Mexican piñatas that kids whack seven bells out of; the kids also blindfolded, as blind as the horses. There they'll be, the horses, all ready and waiting in their thick woven padding, their peto, to protect them from the bull's horns, to ease their fear of seeing the bulls charge, bulls that will lift the horses off their feet. – Animal against animal … it's terrifying, D will say, it's the part that scares you most. There's something wrong with the sight of two vulnerable confused animals set against each other. The sight of the muscle of the bull pushing against all that padding, a quilted blind horse tottering around on spindly legs, or held sideways like that in the air, as if someone had taken that old rocking horse I'd once had and fork-lifted it.

You see how poetic it can get. The ring will be illuminated, spectacular, circus-like. We will be moved to see it lit up like that, protected like that with police and officials, horses, shit everywhere, the buzz and the noise, nowhere to park, circle and circle again, the corrida … It's a party, the sun is an orange ball, such moments, being together, holding hands, eager steps. Posters, plastic bulls of all sizes, the usual selection of fans, all you'd expect spun around candyfloss, black liquorice stuck in the teeth, beer swilled around the edges of the ring, the toilets growing moss, rust, taps running brown water. Beside the toilets, the first aid room, more a small enfermería where some may die. We'll peep in. We'll see that much. – Did we pay to see a man die … D's words will startle me, but I get out of having to answer because the cushion man will be shouting harder than all of us, selling the two-Euro padding for our comfort, for the concrete seats we'll spend hours upon, the rather hard cushions that people will later throw at the matador along with whatever cardigans and jumpers the crowd will have loosely draped around them. The matadors wiping the sweat of the fight from their faces and necks into the garments, throwing them back to the crowd – depending on who is alive or dead that is: the ones left to celebrate with or condemn.

Horses never scared me before, except their height and muscularity that I more respected than feared – but not like this. I'll admit that it will scare me to approach them. Restless, chained up, the stench of green shit, the noise chains make when they are pulled too vigorously, the way horses have of suddenly trying to break free, tossing their heads in fierce jerks, the sound metal makes when chewed between oversized teeth. But it will be the violence of the unexpected red rags obliterating their eyes that will make me hesitate, as if beneath their bindings there are only gaping bloodied sockets that are able still to pinpoint the exact location of caution in my body.

En will go first behind the horses, though it will seem forbidden to cross them in this way. We'll all dither, stare across the divide at En telling us to hurry up! Half-expecting to see a bull charge wildly through the underside of the amphitheatre. Instead the picadors pick their noses, prepare the horses, mount, move their balls in their tight yellow pants. A sorry start.

But I'm rushing ahead …

Go back …

– The bloody bulls will die whether you go to see them or not, En said when we took a tour this morning before the bullfight, just En and me. We'd driven to Madrid early on Sunday morning, the boys deciding they'd meet up with us later, agreeing that we'd buy tickets ready for the evening's fight then we'd all go together. My enthusiastic calls of excitement, nods, animated enough, sure enough, until alone again with En I found myself retracting, admitting that I was not sure yet if I could go through with such a thing, be part of it, the cruelty of it all. En's repetition of *The bloody bulls will die* … puts an arm around my dithering; moral wavering, whichever way you look at it … Let him take it out of my hands and conscience. For now … We won't count the steps we'll take to find the end of a crowd. Tag on to an earlier tour just starting while others still queue up. Postpone for an hour the time when we must commit to this evening's corrida. Look up at the palatial building, walk round and around its fat brick girth, strain necks and eyes, getting camera angles just so, touch the hot metal of sculpted bulls caught in various states of ferocity around the edges of the building. The guide, a young Spanish woman asks, – Who speaks Spanish? Hands up … We oblige, she counts. –Who speaks English? HANDS UP … Obedient like good school children at milk time. Count again; – Italian? More eager straight arms, a few unsure limp hands. – French? A wave or two, only to hear her reply in Spanish that she doesn't speak Italian, won't speak French, so will repeat everything twice, Spanish, English, and people will just have to catch up. Most of the Spanish I figure out, and I use her repetition as an opportunity to make notes, the English translation confirming what I am slow to jot down. Adding that she always begins each new bit of information with, *Well* …

– Well … It's the largest bullring in Spain … The biggest ring can be found in Mexico City … The bulls are especially bred from the age of three on farms, they run wild with horses and men train them with long poles. There are many different ways in Spanish of speaking of a bull. There are forty-five precise words describing the colour of a bull, twenty-one the formation of the horns, and many words to describe the fighting characteristics. The word matador means 'killer'. Lots are drawn the morning of the corrida to determine who will fight which bulls. The bulls are allocated in three pairs to three individual matadors, their teams and impresarios.

I scribbled fast and furiously onto deep pink Post-Its littering my already full notebook. The Post-Its opened out in a fan over a scrawl of notes I will never properly use or form into a story about the bullfight. Didn't Hemingway say it all for us in *Death in the Afternoon*? He was so impressed with bullfighting that he was not able to write about it for five years. *I wish it would have been ten,* he says, reiterating the guide's words, the technical importance of the bull's innocence, of not ever seeing a man on foot. *Only the horses work the bull; this is why they charge the animal and not the man,* Hemingway says ... *otherwise the bull would gain experience in how to cope with unmounted men with capes and thus become unkillable.*

The bull is not something I can easily talk about without falling into the usual traps that I'd hoped to avoid: sensationalism, sentimentality, romantic notions. We'll pay to see death six times when yesterday we simply carried home lemons along the Calle de Limon. An abandoned balloon found us, floated around my feet. A balloon with no child attached. Inside our bags, lemons bounced as we walked briskly to escape the afternoon sun. We barely had time to tap the balloon with our toes, help it on its way, when it sneaked behind us and exploded as we disappeared out of lemon street, end of the street, end of balloon.

It is the yellow of the ring caught in full sun that pulls us close as we continue on our guided tour, mid-morning, the small walk from the cool, dark, rather foreboding outer circle to the inner ring. Some wander ahead, already bored and impatient to get to where the bull will soon stand, run, kill or die. Either way, it is during this slow short walk from outer to inner circle, almost funeral steps, everyone hushed, a dignified respect, that I realise I do want to be here – of course; had I been lying all along? The couple to my side wear matching yellow clothes, a tenuous link, the sharpness of the hour, the clarity of sun, citrus aftershave fresh on the air, my feet on sand sensing the bull, a nervous excitement even while we wait for the bull – who is not yet here; could he be?

We enter the ring and we encounter the bull. I can even smell the bull, my foot scraping at the yellow sand. I am laughing now to myself, laughing at my own gesture to imitate, trying not to let others see that I squat down to touch the sand and for a minute am tempted to write a message for his arrival. I'm laughing again at the whole sorry thought, my mouth opening, heart quickening. He may be here in his dark pen, resting and kept quiet, waiting, not yet knowing where he is and to what end. I have no tail to speak of but feel it would turn and turn again if I looked behind. He's waiting somewhere, in the smell of the horses' shit. An absence then a rush of bullshit takes on a precise taste in the mouth, eased by the faint sound others' feet make upon the yellow grit, arcs intercept straight lines, lines that follow and lose a stranger's trajectory, imprints meet then scatter like the patterns each bull has made as they're dragged out following the kill, all those marks covered over, all the pathways in and out of here scraped clean. Centre stage. This is when I come to know – bull's eye on this hot circle – I know that I will be here this evening.

Still I do not confess this. A tour of an empty bullring is not a decision to proceed to the small window at the front to buy the tickets for tonight's fight. En says – Come, come … pulling playfully at my wrist. Saying nothing does not reverse my following steps. Do I want the blood on my conscience? Too dramatic. – You decide. En's repetition of – *The bloody bulls will die* … third time lucky now. Like the hushed silence as we entered the ring, the outside in, walk toward the light, shade your eyes ahead of the beast, before and after. Move forward but with hesitation in my step. The pig's hesitation that John Berger wrote of in his book *Pig Earth*, a book I was by coincidence reading before the fight. The hesitation Berger speaks of before the pig dies. *All his life the pig had complied. Meme had fed him as if he were a member of the family. [...] Now for the first time he hesitated.* Hesitation that for now is mine, but it is the bull with only hours left, not me; my hesitation is more a ghastly distasteful passivity. – You take me ... Follow En to the ticket office. Stand beside him. Watch. That's how a mother might say it: Watch instead of look. Look and watch ... I am holding En's hand, I wipe the heat around my neck, perfume and sweat mingle. – You decide ... I don't think I want to ... A bleating lie, a bloated hot sweaty lie running between my breasts when all the time I knew En would say – We have to go ... Maybe, then a silent nod of agreement, a betrayal. Retract it quickly ... But if we didn't pay ... Shh ... don't over-egg the tortilla ... Instead, here we are at the ticket office; fingers in unison trace a map behind glass, a price list, colours indicating the right seats, good seats, sun/shade, front rows, good views, just behind the barrera. I offer up my bankcard: things are finally that easy. It's me after all who presses down the pattern of four digits, looking back to witness the tired queue, glad we are here at the front, early enough and paying, agreeing that the bloody bulls – wanting to obliterate the word bloody from the sentence – maybe just part of the delivery, the bloody line. And bloody it will be for sure ...

~

The evening of the corrida we are not really listening as the parade begins. Isn't this how it so often is, the eye trying too hard? Instead, a hand interrupts, pushes me back. D is moving again. – It's not allowed! I tell him. – A man will come and move you to your allotted seat. I keep saying the same thing – It's the rules! Listen to your voice again being such a mother. Watch-with-Mother. Admit it, we're not really watching that attentively when the costumes catch the light, when the black horse rears before the royal box, the matadors bowing, holding

263

their hats to their hearts, when the key is thrown by the official onto the yellow circle under their feet. The key that will open the gate, the toril, from where we'll see the bull for the first time. Instead we are calling again to D who keeps changing his mind, who returns from two flights of steps to reposition himself beside me, behind the picadors. We can almost touch their hats. In our haste to persuade D to agree to sit with us, we miss the name of the first bull, his name written on an enormous chalkboard carried on a stick. There's a man who has the job of carrying the names, a man who turns and turns again inside the circle of yellow sand, like the women who totter on heels at boxing matches holding up the numbers of the round. I never imagined such things here; dressed in an immaculate white shirt and bow-tie, a rather small fat unassuming man holds up with some difficulty the names of each bull. Name, weight, round chalk letters; he twirls, the man with the chalk board, proud of his short but important time in the ring, proud of his curly fragile handwriting, of being in charge of the bull's names, names too easily obliterated with a wipe of his hand as each bull comes and goes.

We're not fast enough, we lose the name of the first bull while disagreeing over the spelling, in our slowness to translate, while Luke passes around the tiny video he's taken on his mobile, D still deciding where to sit, Hugo only managing to call out the bull's weight: 614 kilos. Mid-conversation it's the horns that catch our eye, the light, the bulk and muscle of a live bull. A man behind us gets to his feet and laughs with the relish of a butcher, a butcher in a blue shirt, a man too familiar with flesh, with the ways to cut, keep, discard, empty, hang, pull inside-out. – Torro … Torro, he roars over our heads. We waited for the bull the way one waits for the body at a funeral, or longs for the bride to enter the church, to get that first glimpse, necks twisted, hands clammy, no one else will do, the bride, the corpse, the bull: nothing is more satisfying to the eye after all our anticipation – that for sure is tinged with the shame of knowing what a bull cannot yet understand. It's his vitality and the life in his flesh that are frightening. It's hot, but no time to consider the heat. When at last he arrives, not yet out of breath, both the bull and us are released and trapped as others rise to their feet. Just like it is in church, when you're the only one who's not Catholic and you are minutes behind everyone else. Not that you care; sometimes you sit it out, telling yourself you're not the least bit religious anyway, more curious, that it's more that you like the buildings, rituals – there, here, same thing. The matadors pray, crossing themselves before, during, after crossing the horns of the bull: to kill the bull their body must make the sign of the cross. Here, no one's embracing; still we are the only ones sitting, unsure; sit it out, etiquette dwarfed by others waving, clapping and whistling at the bull. Remembering the earlier words of the guide …

– *Well* … to begin, before the first act starts, footmen – banderilleros or peones – work the bull with large magenta or gold capes. The matador also has to establish the bull's skills, if it favours one horn or the other, hooks to the left or right, or if it swings its horns up when under attack. If a bull is reluctant to fight it can be withdrawn, signalled out with the wave of a green handkerchief.

The wave of a hanky, signalling out.

We come to know this is a lie; we come to know with this very first bull. D worries again that we are too close, that the bull has been known to fly over and into the crowd. – There's a man over there wearing red; red or dead. – It's a lie, about the red; it's the movement and not the colour that the bull charges… Don't believe it, don't believe a word of it. Still the picture replays in your head of the mayhem, of the bull flying over the barrera and – Serve us all right.

Gentle bull. Cute! I want to ask the butcher behind me about the lie of the green hanky. It will never appear. How innocent, to expect them to pardon a docile bull, a bull running out from a dark pen thinking that he was free! How could a bull know, a colour-blind bull, how could it know what is to come? All the handkerchiefs look the same to him. How is he to know that I have forgotten to carry anything resembling a green rag. There is no pardoning this bull, a bull that refuses to fight, a bull that now trots to the centre, looks around with doe eyes at the men taunting him, just stands there nibbling the yellow ground. You might even feel his eyelashes blinking, the way he licks his snout, swishes his tail: bull. His caution makes it worse, the crowd on their feet again, hissing, jabbering, the butcher booing, whistling into my right ear, his protests angrier than anything the bull can muster. But angry he will become, in his own way and fashion, as he must – what else does a bull have left? – Some lie down on the ground, they give up, the butcher's wife says. I've seen it many times. Gentle bull, now whipped up to a kind of ferocity that will never convince. At no time will anyone pardon him.

Have you ever seen a bull balance on his horns? It's not a joke; he rushes, miscalculates, slips, the force and his forward thrust flipping him up into the air, and for a moment he's upright, the bulk of his 614 kilos completely vertical in the air like that, straight up in the air. I am not kidding; the whole body balances and shudders, rigid on two sharp horns. Everyone's laughing ... Not me ... but you would say that. – It's like something from a cartoon, D says, like Cow and Chicken. Not an udder in sight, the weight of course forces him into a somersault. The sound I make that D, Hugo and Luke imitate in unison. Between the mimicry, Hugo whispers to me – Let's leave. Declares to all of

266

us that he thinks we should go. We no doubt look at him, touch his face, but no one answers. There are the familiar sounds that a family makes alongside a cry that comes as the bull falls with a thump that twists his back: my cry, still not his. A beast that size doing a horn stand ... more to come, finding his way to regain some composure, some dignity. Still, no one waves a green hanky, and where would you get such a colour if you'd thought to carry one, dye one, a deep green handkerchief?

– Well... Act one, the picadors come into the ring quite early on, they lance the bull. A metal stirrup like a box they slide their feet into protects the picadors' right legs. The horses were once unprotected; in the past people came to see them being disembowelled. It was said to make the bull feel more confident and the crowds loved it. There was also a superstition that a goring from a horn that had first been sunk in a horse's body would not turn septic and would heal quicker than goring from a clean horn. The bull's neck muscle is raised when it's angry. When he stabs the muscle, the picador is not supposed to tear the flesh nor bear down too forcefully, so as not damage the bull's spine.

Common cart horses, En said when we saw the horses earlier this morning, when the guide ended the tour at a small museum tucked at the back of the ring, avoided the gift shop we'd lost most of the fellow tourists to. The horses on the way, almost reminiscent of some seaside treat. The same horses then disarmed, naked, no costumes – just lined up with their backsides to us, unable to turn. Only one of them allowed eyes-forward, centre-stall; a token horse waiting like us for the bull, maybe with no memory of the bull. Can a horse forget what he is called upon to do here? Take a left at the horses to tour the small museum that gives a potted history of bullfighting, the horses, the blades I so feared; close upon the solidity of metal pics and the curved broken killing sword snapped in two and retrieved from the bulls' flesh. We looked into the faces of famous bulls, beheaded, stuffed and mounted just over our heads, lines of bulls around each wall. – Look at this, En said, and this one, and this one ... They all look so different; you can tell their personalities by the different expressions and colours and sizes. Look at the neck on that one ... look at his eye. They look so cruel. – Can glass be cruel?

– Well ... next, act two, using long sticks decorated with coloured paper, ending in a pointed barb. The peones, working again on foot, run at the bull, then on tiptoes go very close to the horns, stick in the barbs, and dash to one side. The sticks, or banderillas, hang down and decorate the bull. Once they're placed around either side of the muscle this regulates the carriage of the neck and slows the bull down. They must continue to weaken the raised neck muscle and so lower the bull's head so that the matador can later pass the sword over the horns. After the banderillas are placed into the bull he is by now streaming with blood but can still be very powerful and unpredictable. The moves the matador makes with the pink cape, and the sword which holds the cape into shape, are called Veronicas after Saint Veronica who apparently wiped the face of Jesus with a cloth. Before the bull is killed the matador replaces the large cape he uses for a small red muleta and a curved sword. The best matadors bring the bull's body very close to their own body, and make the bull swerve – which weakens its spine. The bull's head is by now hanging very low; his tongue is hanging out. Both man and bull are now held completely still before each other. He may kill the bull by receiving – letting the bull charge him and receiving the bull on his sword – or by diving in with the sword while the bull stands still – or a combination of the two. The spot where the matador's sword enters the bull at the back of the neck is no bigger than a large coin between the bull's shoulder blades. In order to kill the bull the matador must move his left hand across his body with the muleta at the crucial moment to draw the bull's head to the right while moving over the top of the bull's horns, pushing the sword deep into the space between the cervical vertebra with a quick downward thrust into the main aorta.

The first bull falls to his knees. Death is finally swifter than our eyes that try to keep up. His legs fold under him, but for some moments his upright bulk gets stuck in a sitting position; between life and death the bull looks more like a cherished ornament feigning sleep. If they all died that easily, the butcher's wife says ... if they all got the sword up to the hilt. To the hilt: the expression goes as deep as the curved sword, a surprisingly soundless death, the sudden weight of a bull knocked to one side from a collective shove, no more than a few ballet pumps to haunches and belly, four legs thrown up – eight, counting the bull's, that are splayed open. Coda, coming from Cauda, Latin, meaning Tail. I wanted to touch the bull – not a dead bull, more when he came into the ring... I said so but no one replied. I didn't repeat myself, or admit that I didn't have the guts, the mother's milk, the stomach or the grok for repeating, or touching, or knowing how to approach.

Ask yourself, did you want to see the death of a bull once, twice, six times especially, no reply, dumb questions normally not so viole[n]t. One death could be excused, one death could maybe have slipped by and been written off, blagged or put down to curiosity, but six bulls in one sitting seemed a concession to interest. I knew that, I read the books ... later. I read little in advance, a few pamphlets, mostly in Spanish. I missed a lot of what they said; it can happen to the best of tourists. It is expected of tourists, all kinds of tourists, to want to see this – it's what people *do* here when they visit.

One bull down and I can now say that I know what to expect; one bull down and dragged through the dragging gate. Look at the marks he makes through the sand, blood-smeared, the curved white lines breaking apart as he is taken on his way to tomorrow's menu del dia – and now what? What is my excuse to stay… We've paid! – Not good enough. Each death is never the same twice…

D, as if reading my thoughts, becomes animated about the time we heard the pigs being killed in Spain. Another holiday, south of Granada, over Christmas. Yes. We were eating goat for Christmas dinner. Pigs, goats, it gets confusing, a right old butcher's block. Remember the goat I'd also seen by accident on a mountain top, that morning when I turned at the wrong moment through our open car window – wrong or right, depends how you look at it – when I turned to see a man holding a young goat between his firm thighs, the head twisted in my direction, the man running his knife across the kid's throat. I was the last thing the goat saw. I didn't say a word to anyone else, not then; thankfully they were all looking the other way. – Remember the pig, D says. Yes, the rattling of pails, the squeals and commotion, later the inebriation that went on for hours and then silence. The silence we wished for and then didn't know what to do with when it finally came.

We watch the ears and tail being cut from the bull, from bull to matador, the matador who walks around the ring holding them up before passing them to the picador who throws them in to the callejon, pushes them into the ground with his foot, hiding the evidence that sand resists. I look down at the useless ears and I worry that the bull may still have been alive when they were removed – half-dead and alive – not possible, but I am sure I saw his eye move as his ear was crudely carved off. I

270

wonder about the missing tail, think of us after the guided tour looking for rabo de torro, nothing like the oxtail soup we'd eaten as children. Father's favourite when he was unwell, oxtail in a mug. At home we also make the rabo, buy the thick tails from the local halal butchers. The recipe always invites slow cooking, up to seven hours. Flour the tail. Fry. Add carrots, onions, celery, bay leaves, stock; drain off the fat midway, add in more white wine as required, fresh thyme. We searched for the rabo de torro earlier today, the size of the beast, and why choose a tail from all that flesh. When I ate I did not think of the bullfight to come as the waiter from Columbia shouted, – Muy rico, Muy rico, Bueno ... kissing his finger and thumb into the air; our smiles of agreement. Pass more bread, we called; mop up the gravy, suck out the marrow, the jelly is the best part, add salt and agree it is easier to eat with your hands, compare the patterns the bones make, reform the shape of a tail around the edges of your plates, share each other's spinach, patatas pobres dusted in paprika. I was not passive when it came to the tail.

It takes just twenty minutes, they say, to kill the bull – well, to perform the three acts that end with his death. The final act is to be executed in less than twelve minutes; any more and the bull is reprieved, so they say – no certainties like the absence of the green hanky. Death rarely works in one clean movement.

The pig fights intelligently, JB writes. En agrees that they have intelligent eyes. Horses, we say, have kind eyes, beautiful eyes; cows' eyes are gentle. I do not consider a chicken's eyes as anything but shifty, neurotic – you could say that something is always about to happen to a chicken. The bull's eyes are ... what? From here, and with the second bull, a younger, friskier but more daring bull already streaming with blood, already pierced, barbed, decorated, act three, a bull so quickly upon the point of death – I insist on keeping my eyes open out of a kind of misplaced respect. Make a silent pact with myself not

271

to cover my eyes from the kill, not to shy away from the sword and the descabello, the short straight sword they will use to stab the head or neck of the bull if the matador fails too many times to get the killing sword accurately between the shoulder blades. How can my eyes from such a distance see the eyes of a bull? Yet I am sure again I see them red, the eyes of the second bull that won't die; I swear his eyes are red, the weary, bewildered, obedient bull. The sound he makes, like the pig, the sound of his cry that fills the arena, that makes me want to cover my ears as the bull falls, and squeals turn to mews, a noise that continues, a noise that makes you want to shout, – No, fools! That makes you want to jump the barrera, take the knife, find a way to stop the sound a lung makes when it's pierced.

Bull two, dragged out by the harnessed team of mules, is soon followed by bull three ... and so on ... decoration and leverage, horns and a tail pulled together like a tug of war. The pulled tail looks too fragile to stay put, too thin to sustain a cooking pot and a family of four. The bull that gives up just sits, legs tucked under, eyes blinking, reminiscent of some huge cow too full with milk. They kill bull three swiftly with the descabello. Hugo will say, – Excitement can quickly turn to boredom here, the repetition numbs you in the end. Bull four, or was it five already to come, the sound of the trumpet again, everyone repositioned, the spring-cleaning of the arena, the blood they try each time to rake away, to collect in a small basket with two handles, soft large weave, like a basket in which you'd carry a newborn baby. One footman brushes back the surface of the circle after each fight, scrapes up the bloodied sand, buries it to one side of the barrera, working hurriedly with his foot, the deftness of his foot freshening the meaning of his given name. Another footman re-limes the white lines with a metal contraption on wheels.

I would like to hold the chalkboard, be responsible for the

line, see if I am capable of marking a steady sweep. The stray sawn-off ears continue to pile up under the picadors' boots, sand sticks unevenly to fur. The crowd restocks itself with snacks. A man feeds his baby daughter churros. People kiss and call to one another. Men rush off behind the scenes to take a swift piss while the animal's fear pissed into sand dries and disappears in the heat. By the time the last of the bulls is in the ring I notice that the lights have come on and that the sun has already been replaced by a full moon, as if the circle of dark purple sky is no more than a scene change at an opera. The costumes of light sparkle more. The colour of the bull deepens, as does the circle of yellow it occupies. We give ourselves over again to the whiff of other people's cigar smoke and whisky fumes that waft over us while the second bull's death-cry still haunts the air. Being on the side of the bull does not make it better. Try not to lose count or concentration, try not to ask, – What number bull are we on now? We get the hang of it, as they say, the gist; the more it continues, the more seamless and laborious it can get. On it goes.

Hemingway writes …

At this point it is necessary that you see a bullfight. If I were to describe one it would not be the one that you would see, since the bullfighters and the bulls are all different, and if I were to explain all the possible variations [...] that would be interminable [...] So with any book on mountain ski-ing, sexual intercourse, wing shooting [...] it being always an individual experience, there comes a place [...] where you must say do not come back until you have skied, had sexual intercourse [...] or been to a bullfight so that you will know what we are talking about.

Isn't that how it feels to continue to try to describe this, to go on with bull four, five, six … to reach for the etceteras, for the ellipsis … And is it true that throughout I have kept my eye

273

on the bull and had no care for the man? – Why else come, En says, if you don't think that the man might get killed. Yes, admit it, don't we secretly want to see that too? If it's all so one-sided, all so easy, then what's the point? The coincidence of the conversation, the lull, the crowd too quickly turning to unrest – here the order of things is everything, and time is only a trumpet note away, a warbling note that reminds everyone that the repetitive call to kill can too quickly lose its patience.

Old hands clap now, clap out slow time. At first I don't know what this means. Until someone translates that the protests from the crowd mean that they think the matador is taking too long to kill the bull. That he is indulging himself too much. Is that it? Abandoned Olés, some jeers and calls to finish it. – Get on with it, the butcher yells. A repetitive clap becomes one while the matador holds out his hands in a gesture of mocking surprise. The bull, locked into a half-turn, as always waits; the matador takes his position, unknowing that as he flirts with the crowd, exchanges the bloodied pink cape for the small red muleta and killing sword, that he accidentally kicks over his hat, the hat he earlier placed onto the sand, face-up. – Luck turned over, the butcher says. – Superstitious nonsense, his wife replies. While in the middle of a charge, the cape commanded firmly, the bull does what we paid to see but by now have forgotten to expect: he catches the matador with his right horn; he flicks him up and into the air, a body turning as if caught inside a tombola, a body that glitters more than ever as it turns under the lights, a body that now seems so tiny, limp, round and round he goes like a little circus trick.

It is only for seconds we consider the man is dead, a death swiftly postponed by the spectacle of fresh magenta capes flapping away at the bull as footmen rush in to carry the matador over their heads and out to the side of the ring. There is an endless hush. A collective inhaled breath. A bull waits. The laboured panting of the bull's body and the way he so quietly watches reminds me that I must remember to look at him, that it would be too easy to forget him for the minutes that the men confer. All we have taken for granted of the matador's skill, an unspoken wish: you cannot deny that you wanted to see this. The bundle of men part, lift the matador back to his feet and support him into the ring, waft him with smelling salts like a line of altar boys let loose with a cloud of incense. Soon he is let go by a dozen hands that linger still as he takes his first baby steps, wobbles, finds his balance, advances, limping back to look at the bull – not with malice, more with a sense that they are bound now into something that must be seen through.

Beneath the roar of the now-exulting crowd, the bull – who sniffed the ground as he entered earlier, sniffed the exact spot where the previous bull fell – pees a silver stream into the yellow light. Under the smirking moon, perfectly positioned on the chalk line, the turn of the cape, the arch of the body, the sharp twists of the bull's spine, the ache in our backs – it comes full circle: the blood of the bull shines; the blood darkens on the suit of the matador, like the beautiful linen shirt we saw at the museum on the tour, the carefully folded camisa lit up in glass. Trying to make sense of the embroidered shirt, the delicate lace. En saying – Someone died in that shirt … Look at the blood, he said. Ivory one side, the heart side darkened with now-brown blood, buttons dividing a heart long stopped. JB describing the pig's eye as intelligent, *His arse as tiny as a buttonhole …* like the buttonhole of the camisa. As I watch a circle of men huddle around a falling bull, botch his death, I am not thinking of pig or matador or the circumference of his arse, I am instead wondering what a bull's heart weighs. I recognise the lost poise, unintentional, of men who now look no better than the boys round the back alleys: pathetic, the way they collectively finish the last bull with a blade turned in his skull, the way I feel

275

changed and sullied, in the back of my notebook the listed names and weights of the dead bulls, complete.

– Ignominious, En says, to be dragged out like that by three mules, by men in crisp white shirts, red bands flying, a lassoed whip cracking on the air. Ignominious their haste, the harness of tiny bells, a bull with a length of rope around its neck like tatty parcel string, the stamped arse of a delivered bull, and the ribbon he still wears, prettied up for the night.

Georgie's letter

I've been trying on and off to do this – write about written, violent threats that happened to me. I almost feel to call them violent is not right, so they are never expressed, hidden; trying to write them becomes complicated and difficult and so you come against a self-resistance...

It's really caught my thoughts,

See you later x

K's letter to Xavier

There are letters that I write and do not show. I keep them and recite and refine and try hard to get each one right. I can reason with you; I thought it all through today when I was at work. I can understand now how to sort this out; how to answer your questions. I am lying on the floor by the sofa, I see toast crumbs around its edge, and carpet fluff, hear next door coming home, kids outside going past on their bikes. I am trying to answer your questions, Xavier. I write you a letter two sides of A5, the paper is red; it takes me two hours forty minutes. I walk to your house along the streets; it is dark. Through your window I see you. You are smoking and watching TV. I post the letter through the door. I walk home past the cars, pubs and houses, through the night. On Monday morning I see the letter in your kitchen bin torn up into red flakes over pouches of Golden Virginia and Yorkie wrappers. You are upstairs. I reach into the bin and shred the pieces some more, I tear the pieces of letter small as small, push them to the bottom. Wash my hands in the sink. Everything is ok.

Day Pages – Spain

In Adrada de Pirón, we tease the sheep, En and me, all three boys still asleep at our temporary home. Sit and take photographs beside the fountain. Behind us the old school we'd like to buy. Sheep gather around as if we know the way to a land they have misplaced. Dozens of sheep, but we are very much awake, protect our open eyes by refusing to count. The anonymity of sheep: they all look alike; the anonymity we have again begun to take for granted. Anonymity, get used to saying the word, like something you'd write for a birthday wish, or your butcher's list – 3lbs of rump end and some best cut of anonymity.

For now, we part the sheep, who are trying to wrap En and me in a kind of blue wool coat – wool and reassurance not needed here in this heat, in this hidey hole; maybe a sheep's way of saying goodbye, of rubbing goodbye into our legs, wool station; in the early sun with the sheep for company we discuss the date and time for returning home, to begin again.

Walking together over the hilltops, walk the same road as we have for the weeks we've been hidden away. As usual, once far enough away from the house, we deviate from the road and are pulled toward yellow fields filled with stones. Imagine having the job of clearing all these stones, *piedras*; say, it's not worth it, moving all these stones, trying to cultivate this land where the best soil is in the dip. Pass a cart with a missing wheel. Stop walking where the road forks, indecision already turns you home. Home turns you right back on yourself. Pass the cart again. Stop again and admire the distance you've travelled, the silver of the sky, imagine painting with such a pale palette, until you turn and face the sun and the sky deepens as if your eyes were fooling you only a moment ago.

Not alone, we find ourselves sliding down a bank littered

with white bones, surrounded now by a new flock of sheep – only this time dead, scattered into parts, odd bits of ribs, leg bones, spinal columns cushioned by the grass, straw and broken-up tools, metal pick-axes, rusted spades, a perfect horse's skull. Say how rare it is to find this. The sight of the bones makes us feel we have intruded on a scene we should not have been party to, a kind of carnage. We do not ask what has happened here as we would not be able to do more than speculate: dogs, poison, slaughter for meat. Still, we take the horse's skull. Carry it home, bleach it whiter than it already is. Worry that it will be confiscated at Customs, a skull wrapped in our clothes, X-rayed at the airport. – No one say a word. D will draw the skull, reluctantly this time. The word for bones between us all week: *huesos*. One picture bringing back another. Way back, when D was not yet two, he scribbled something, something that absolutely resembled a horse's skull. No question of it, we said, and framed the stamp of an image, a skull that came from a toddler's imagination; all that cannot be replicated, the decision and precision of lines, of a head being formed, a horse's skull emerging in crayon.

Returning through the yellow field, En tells me that last night he dreamt of yellow flowers. I tell him that last night yellow flowers were the final thing I read about before I slept: an old woman picking yellow flowers in Sam's story, old hands picking yellow flowers for a grave, the coincidence of yellow flowers between us on the pillow. The sky now the Sam-same piercing silver-blue as Beckett's eyes.

These final days in Spain.

The ease with which we take to these streets, roaming along what we now call our usual routes; so soon we set up patterns and repetitions, small maps, trails we make, create a sense of direction, survey, look! Sweep up the remains of a rabbit, rabbits later chosen in a small mountain store. Creatures everywhere.

Departing from the sheep, we buy rabbits. Rabbits we'll buy for today's lunch as well as an order to take home. Home. The small store we pop into each morning after coffee, just En and me. The order for rabbit, the order of each day, the routine we so love, the day beginning with our early morning walk to the village, coffee in the shade, read, write, sometimes buy bread from the bar, more often from the store, choose meat, handle and discuss the vivid colour of vegetables, dried beans in buckets – push your hand into the coolness while no one looks. All the women carry baskets. I am no exception here.

We wait our turn at the back of the tiny room, En and me. We sit among the small boxes of local wine, sacks of rice. Inhale the powdered bread that is being baked out the back. Watch the two women work in their sleeveless tabards; their arms are brown and their muscles tense and relax as they work. Daydream of touching their arms as they slice the *jamon*, weigh the cheese, lay out the jamon in strips, patterned inside waxed paper. To feel the care and work an arm gives as they begin again with each customer. She parcels the meat as if it were a present, with string she winds and cuts from a long reel. We wait our turn for the rabbits. The only other time I ate rabbit was when my grandfather brought one home, complete with fur and ears, an expression of defeat in the grimace of the rabbit's mouth; grandfather's expression was I-told-you-so, and how much the gift pleased him, the gift of rabbit passed on. Remember Mother saying, it was like cutting up a cat, the cat that surely ate the rabbit, while she, the lady in the shop, cuts the pale pink flesh into quarters. It was caught only hours ago, she explains, proud of how fresh these rabbits are, asking if we want the heads. The skinned head of the rabbit red with blood as if it were blushing over some last thought. We look at each other and in unison say, No! to the heads, then hesitate and think that maybe we should have said Yes.

We'll freeze the rabbits and carry them home in a bag. – I'll prepare them for tomorrow, she says, the lady in the shop, for Wednesday. To pick up the rabbits on Wednesday, – *Miércoles*, we all say together, two rabbits that will travel home at an altitude of 30,000 ft. Two rabbits that will cause our cases to be overweight so that in front of a long tired queue of eyes we'll have to take them out of our luggage; carry the rabbits by hand onto the plane. The wrapped-up rabbits stuffed beside the duty free wine and perfumes. Look up the recipe E sent way back: seep the rabbit in vinegar overnight, add pickling spices, garlic, onion, carrots – there's the joke … The woman in the shop will translate the word for celery … *apio*. I love it when the whole shop joins in.

I am sent a postcard called *The Passer-by*.

I am sure the person who sent it wasn't thinking of you, wasn't considering what was going on, past tense. Maybe it was something I would have worried over when we first got your letter. – When I look at the image it looks sinister, R says. She is passing *The Passer-by* around the table. We read the greeting and for sure it was from a well-meaning friend. No harm meant. We are around the old faithful table again. There are fresh flowers, food, wine, the time of day casting shadows in the room, onto the image on the card, *The Passer-by*. A tree partly obliterates the man who has walked by the other. On the road, to the side of the pavement where they have passed, a Stop sign is illuminated as if the moon were full and visible to both men if they only cared to look up. Maybe not the moon, maybe a passing car passing the passers-by, illuminating the Stop sign. Both men are in motion, how else to pass by, but the man at the right hand side of the card is on the point of running, turning his head back toward the man whose has passed him and is now, in part, obliterated by the tree. The man he looks back at hurries on, his hands shoved deeply into his trouser pockets. Not sure if this was a gesture that he made before, during or since he passed by the other. We can assume that the man racing ahead is hiding something in his trouser pockets, protecting something, holding something. We could assume that he said something as he passed by the man who now turns back to look at him, startled. There's hesitation, fear, regret, a question to be asked, a change of heart – or does the man turning recognise the other and has only just realised …

Last week we could have passed you. You could say that once your letter arrived we passed you every day, real and imagined, that potentially you were everyone we passed and didn't know. You, the most intimate of strangers to whom I try to tell everything, even at the expense of sounding foolish, even if to say that I can say, hand on heart, that we will never know, can't ever, won't ever know, whether last week we passed you or not.

For now...

Let's say...

What if En and I were walking home quite briskly, it was threatening rain. A blustery day; let's make it a Saturday. You were with a woman. You were not the woman. You were to the left of the woman as En was to my left, two men, him and you, passing each other by. You looked sheepish – is that the word? You looked nothing like I imagined, but there again, if I had to try and describe to you what I imagined of your face, that would soon come to nothing. Still, I can say you looked older, frailer, greyer, more worn down, more insipid than the picture I had made of you. En was carrying an umbrella, rolled up, a long black umbrella that had belonged to his father. He didn't smile or wave, but raised the umbrella in the air as a gesture to acknowledge, the way someone might doff a hat. We said nothing. I asked nothing, the umbrella like a weapon raised and then not used. Water threatens to fall, umbrellas remain rolled, for now, are raised and lowered, we pass by in seconds.

I bit my lip, I told En, – I don't know why but when we passed that man, I felt a little guilty when I saw you raise the umbrella, when I saw it was a gesture of goodwill; wondered if you knew one another or not, the man and you. I don't think the woman even noticed any of it. She was elsewhere in her mind, she was thinking of other things, dreaming of happier days; maybe it was for her the happiest of days – one can never assume the worst. When we passed you, I made a kind of grimace and didn't smile at the time, thinking that I should have, a smile I'd normally give up to any stranger he'd acknowledge, friend or foe, a smile at least between us. No words as we pass. I had no

284

idea who or what or if... Not then; words, those lands of my fathers, slipped by as we passed one another. If you haven't got anything nice to say, my father would always tell us, then say nothing. Wash your mouth out with soap – another expression given up, heard less often now. This threat with soap never carried out, only meant to taste bad, to tease, terrify at times. I would think about all those mouths foaming, frothing, the burn, what kind of soap and perfume? Even if we were to meet, I can honestly say I make a promise: that regardless of the words between us, the soap would stay firmly in the dish.

Not that I think we will meet. Well, despite the imaginative petit-fours that have been passed across the table between us, neither do I think you'll visit. Not really, not now. *Not that I wanted you to, don't get me wrong* – but wasn't that always the threat? How else to turn hurt into a visit, to come over, turn up at the door, your face unannounced calling *Yoo-hoo* round the back. Still, the window cleaner has been; bruised ribs aside – and I'll get to that soon – he's meticulous with the glass. If truth be known, with the passing of time I am glad for you to remain a figment of whatever battered crêpes and cream buns my imagination cooks up for the guests. Even though visiting is welcomed, your visit would require a different sort of doilied terminology, but there again... *Visiting: to shoot the breeze; confabulate, travel to and from; chewing the meat fat, the cud; to inflict: from visitation – to bother, to haunt.*

When I was small, in winter the snow would drift up to the doors, and on such days there would be few visitors. But wanted or not, some always broke through. Father would dig us out early each morning. We'd watch and help too. Help him shovel the snow from here to there. We'd have him home from work and that always made things special; we'd shovel and clean away the snow. He made hard work fun. People didn't visit as they do now. Visiting has become more popular, a new

285

generation, and also a lifetime of visits forgotten.

When people visit I like to cook. Maybe you do too. It's the greeting and the fussing over people that counts. We are often found boiling, braising, rolling, scooping, trimming, presenting. Rabbits to come and oxtail aside, in those early days of the letter I took to cooking goose with apples. Something in your letter wanted me to exceed with all I prepared, to go further in my choice of recipes. To go back to what's safe in the choice of a bird. Tradition. The skin pricked, the flour rubbed over the breast, the perfume of sage and orange oil rising with the heat; all that's held inside a cavity, inside neat-neat stitches. Geese that would chase me as a child when Father took us out walking, calling into the tiny pub in the middle of the fields, with no more than an outhouse where the men would come to relieve themselves between pints, my brother and me too young to be let into the taproom, the whole thing no more than the size of a tiny two-up, two-down. There we'd be wandering the fields with our usual weak shandy and token packet of crisps, playing with the geese. Except we came to know that geese cannot be played with: *they* play with *you*, they bite, chase, worry you, make you spill the lemon-beer, abandon the crisps to them as ten or more ganders gather speed and confidence. They had an arrogance I lacked back then, taste aside, the white feathers long gone; years later, delicious enough, the oven is not my revenge.

I try to imagine you cooking a roast for the family, yet if I think of you cutched up under your own goose-down quilt next to the wife, you smell of heterosexuality and hair wax, the old-fashioned kind. Let's say that your shirts are pristine. That for a treat you do, after all, like to cook most Sundays: lunch for your wife and the kids. There are kids. You are fertile. The children do well in school. You could say that you are and always have been a regular family, more or less the same as us;

in many ways people don't differ that much. You have a dog; we have a cat and a dead canary. The cat is innocent, the canary now under the ground in some forgotten spot. You take the dog for a walk. Our cat sees to himself. There have been a few dogs coming and going in this tale, mostly strays, mostly unhinged, but when you went to post the letter, way back, I realise now that I forgot to write in the dog. I gave the dead man a dog, I gave the scene in which you posted the letter a dog – a stray roaming the night – but I forgot about your pet, no name, just a *Here Boy*; a pronoun, a whistle that becomes a habit over time, that time when I'd imagined you walking to the letter box, that far back, when the dog looked up, surprised to see you still awake at such an hour. Your dog half-asleep and cosy on his chewed Scotty blanket, feeling obliged to look interested and to play the part of a dog. In the end you walked alone to the letterbox … but that was then and this is now.

Maybe, after all, I'll find you at the stove – yes, back to the kitchen… Maybe, like me, it relaxes you to chop, squeeze, pour, measure and stir away all those worries that build up in the week, to lose yourself in the work it takes to make a good Sunday roast. Beef is your favourite; most never consider a goose outside of Christmas, most stick to the unquestioned ritual of rotating Sundays between lamb, chicken, beef. I personally never eat cows; cows are for fawning over, for confiding in; things that walk off over the fields, things licked and protected and ambled around. I never touch milk, but when you slice the beef your gravy's thick, you share out equally the good fluffy Yorkshires, crisp roasts, soft inside; minted peas that steam, all fresh from the soil. You have an allotment you share. You even have a glasshouse and keep the stone in your pocket. You plant beets because they are your wife's favourite; bring home a cabbage you clean free of grubs; the sorrel's run to seed – still, you hum while you work. The letter in you now, back then, a letter you never speak of, not to your wife, nor your elderly dad, especially not to the kids. The dog knows, but stays schtum; no, you do not mention the letter to your fellow growers, not even to the odd passer-by, and rarely to yourself ever again.

The window cleaner calls.

As I said, he has a bruised rib. He calls every fortnight, which this time happens to fall on the day before we are to leave for our trip to Spain. Days of cleaning that he adds his final flourish to, the past events and concern swilled away with the smell of lemon, with the mop and duster and bleach and lavender polish. *Is it that easy?*

The window cleaner explains about the fights or scraps, as he calls them, he'd get into at school. How he has taught his young daughter to box so that she can keep herself safe, how it was her blow last night, while they sparred in their kitchen, that lead to his injury, to his struggle up the ladder while I hold the bucket. I don't mention you or the letter even though I think he would have liked the story, *for the craic*, as he'd say ... While he finishes cleaning the grime from the fronts and makes his way slowly round to next-door, a man calls to collect the panic alarm we've had for months. – All's quiet on the Western front, he says...

I dismantled it that morning, the alarm, from beneath the TV; cleaned away the dust that had formed around the rectangle it left. The wires, too many to tame, just shoved unceremoniously into the plastic bag I grabbed. It wasn't planned, but the message on the bag read *Plastic bags blow, time to say goodbye*. I didn't know if the alarm man would see the joke, if we'd have time to ponder and read it together. In the end there is no time for us to laugh over the message, to talk about the feeling that empty space left under the TV. That *what if* ... What if this is our time out of the wood ...

I don't know why I expected a slower handover, but when the man collects the alarm he is swift, jovial, happy in his work. Says he is glad we didn't need to use it. He doesn't cross the line from the front door into the house. I would have been happy to see the window cleaner hobble off round the back, to make the alarm man tea, to discuss the ins and outs of his alarming job, to let him know I am both ready to give back the alarm and still want to keep it there under the TV. The handover takes a second. – No news is good news, he says, giving me a warm smile as he rushes back to his van, the engine still running.

Somewhere you are sitting, walking, working, eating, resting, loving, lying – not, I presume, at the same time, but whatever you are doing, I am hoping that you can't know how clean, how naked that space beneath the TV now looks. You and me, let's say, sitting down for a moment in two distinct places, unoccupied rooms, moments, intervals. For now I tell you, I press my palm into that area of nothing, the place and time between two points an absent alarm has left, watch the cat sniff my hand as he had, months back, so carefully examined the alarm on its arrival. I give him only minutes before I fill what's unoccupied as full as possible with films and books, any old stack of titles I can find; I do not ask the cat if he considers who will use the alarm next, who will now start where we end – or is that begin? – do not ask if a cat can wander that far.

Day Pages – Spain

Reading HC's *Love Itself in the Letter Box*. Note down that her book ends with... *I don't want to forget, but I don't want to remember. But there is no master for forgetting or for remembering.* The book ends with *Kartoffelpfannkuchen. That means: I love you in the language of potatoes. I hope they are still hot.*

To end with potatoes, cooked ones at that. To end with love as so many letters are signed off.

To begin with a bed, the bed where I first received your words; to finish by stripping the temporary bed, the borrowed bed inside the gold room, the bed that will be made up again with hospital corners, clean white sheets smoothed down by another's hands. My job is only to strip the bed back to its mattress, shake imprints from the feather pillows, gather books with their underlined quotes, what's left beside the bed, this side, that side – even here – a bed stripped causes an odd white goose feather to float through the morning, through a dream. Remember the other night – did I tell you? – I ask En while we finish packing, clearing up, remind him of the bed that was under the sea. Not the sea under the bed, but a wave just held there mid-ocean, an ocean that looked as minty-fresh as a toothpaste commercial. To begin with we are on the shore, but as is so often the case in dreams we do not stay put in one spot; we have points of view that we could not imagine awake. This is how is starts: we are waving out to sea, maybe waving to a ship way off, our feet sinking into sand, our wave just held, the wave of our hands and the wave of water never completed. Under the sea everything is possible and visible, the usual shoal, the usual debris people abandon, toss overboard, the normal infinity of pebbles washed smooth, a few feet kicking, splashing dogs – can a dog cock a leg under the sea? – underwater two

291

people kiss and not a sound is heard, our breath and hands held pointing at the enormous wave, not threatening to crash to our feet. We are almost floating now over the scene; we have shifted and are in both places at once, on the shore and looking right into the ocean, way in the distance where the wave began to gather speed, find its fullness, its call to descend, the wave held back, arrested, giving us a view of … what's that? What point comparisons: it was a bed, nothing more or less. See it, under the sea, immersed, clear as the sun lighting the scene, not a water-bed – who could have known – but a great king-sized bed. And not just that: a bed so neatly made up with a red counterpane – what a word – coverlet – give me another – eiderdown, blood-red, *no symbols where none intended*. Here under the sea an enormous bed – satin-dressed, someone had seen to that; the red had a sheen to it, and on the bed, matching red pillows, so carefully arranged. Someone was neat and it wasn't me, as I had never before seen such a bed; maybe it was just a little like the ones we saw, those red gold and blue beds where Dali and Gala slept, luscious, palatial beds, and at the centre of this dream-red-bed-head what did we see laid out. Not a corpse, but a white piece of paper just placed on the pillow, no visible words. We agreed that we were too far away to read anything into a bed; maybe the sea, the salt, had caused the words to run clean away. The bed was not floating away like the door I dreamt about – remember that? This bed was steadfast and proud of itself, steadfast, embedded into the seabed … ah, what number of beds upon beds.

The now-stripped bed in the gold room looks unassailable, indifferent to our coming and going, to the layers of turning and reading and writing and love-making and scratching. Even the odd death that must have occurred here, well before we climbed in weeks back. Considering the number of strangers piled upon strangers this mattress has held up from one month to the next: the traces are lacking. Only a single tear in the mattress – the single hole in the white veil of mosquito net that will remain unfound. Take a last look around as a way of saying goodbye to a room we will never again occupy. Shove to the edges of the floor the sheets and damp towels we've piled around the room. The gold room's calm indifference to whatever new holidaymakers will soon arrive. Admit that here we've become used to not turning around while we walk; become used to the unlocked doors and windows; become used to not listening out for anything more than the night crickets and the odd mosquito who found his way into our net, the rhythm of one another's stories read out some evenings. Agree not to talk about what's happened any more once we get home: home where, outside of this book, we agree that your letter will be something lost to rendition, to anecdote, to *that time when*. Agree to forget to remember your letter lost somewhere in the outhouse, tucked beside the weed killer and the dried-up door paint. Or should we leave your words here inside an oversized wardrobe, behind three mirrors: a letter folded up as small as possible. Is that its final destination, or could I push it inside a mattress, a small folded page deep inside the tear, inside the curled-up springs, inside someone else's home and country, inside a single summer, or do I lie … lie underneath a bed frame, tuck words up high – on my back in the dust, again to leave one bed for another.

To leave a gold room to memory, a holiday that we say must end with a sighting of the sea, the tilt of the world, the pull of the tides. Seek out instead the dream bed, the sea with no care for who visits its edges, the sea pleasing only itself. Waves come and go, people come and go. Drive early morning to the sea, all that way: look at that! To look early evening for the red bed – long gone, *as if it ever existed*. Instead, remember that time when D looked out at the sea and asked us where the plug was. Tiny boy, to pull the plug on the ocean and not a yellow duck in sight, the sea sloshing memory from here to there, the ebb and pull people bring moved from one land to another.

Memories come back here, memories shared as we all sit together in the small fishing quarter where each time we come back we say, – One day we will buy a small house just over there, that one, no, that one, we will, just wait, right here, a house that will look out to sea. The house barely a house, just two small rooms one above the other, a balcony, fishing nets hung out for mending. We'll eat here, of course we will, then, now, last supper … ha! Wine, fish, bread, salad, sliced oversized tomato, bread torn apart. Salt pinched between finger and thumb. Yes, this evening one of us has the job of salting the fish, squeezing the lemon; another pours the olive oil. Douse, there's a word for you. Douse the fish and the fingers working to prepare the meal. Your mouth fills. There are potatoes too. I haven't forgotten that a potato can end a book, or this letter to you, mouth watering on a potato, fried thick white salted. Salivating over flakes of fish. There's a breeze unexpected that flaps at the paper cloth we have to hold down with pebbles. Together we dunk the torn bread into oil, yellow sopped bread taken to our mouths, chins glistening. D, Hugo and Luke, already satisfied, wander off as if they remember how to play, and do. Only Luke now replaces the word *play* for the words *walk, smoke*. They call it a walk and comb the beach, climb inside beached fishing boats dotted here and there, smoke rising while young men form sand into shapes, forget we are watching when they chase the gulls. Overhear a woman ask, – Were you dreaming of my voice? – Yes, the man says, I was in the sea and I was steered to safety by the sound of your voice …

En and me walking to the rocks; watch the two children, not ours, most likely brother and sister, spitting at the birds beneath to make them fly from the safety of their crevices and ledges to take to the sky in fierce patterns. Swirl and return, spit, and take off again. – It makes you dizzy to watch them, the boy says. – And how do they know when to turn like that in synch, at that speed? – Look at that whale, she says, look at the way the sea is making a perfect enormous white whale from the scum... If you squint it's like Ahab's Moby Dick just under the water. – Call me Ishmael, the boy laughs.

En translates while we climb the rocks with someone else's children just to get a better view, just to point below with them and say, Look! An exact tail, blowhole, tiny eye; photograph one another because we want to and so we do, hold the camera away from gummy smiles exaggerated like the foam whale. Today the sea looks like a caricature of itself, the sun strikes over it, swollen, deep green sea, as if D had crayoned it, placed on top, a ship, a tall proud vessel coming into view. Point and say, – It's like the dream, but still not a red bed in sight. It's also like the napkins D would make at home from paper or fabric, napkins in the shape of tall ships. This ship has funnels with red stripes and black portholes, and there's grey smoke billowing behind, there's a dwarfed fishing boat following as if it were pulled along by a rope, yes, the ship looks as if D folded the ship from linen or drew it all, the whole scene the colour of crayon.

Home coming; we pick up speed, both the ship and the words that search for something to tell you at the end, some flourish, some little scene, something that will let you know I have little left to say.

– I hate metaphors, I tell En, but now look at that damn ship sailing off ... to where? It has passengers, a swimming pool. People are writing letters to loved ones. People are rubbing sunscreen over their noses and shoulders and one another's back. People are making love behind portholes. Sleeping on the deck. Deck chairs – never thought of the meaning before, how literal, deck chairs flapping on a breeze. – No, En says, it's more of a tanker, no passengers; crew hands, mess hall, darts matches, naked breasts sellotaped to bunk walls; camaraderie aside, the stench of homesickness, vomit, hard liquor, piss, sperm, oil and cigars, and not necessarily in that order. The vomiting comes last.

– I drew a sketch of you once, I tell En, do you remember? – On the first trip we took from Plymouth to Santander, on deck, in our deck chairs facing each other. After some time people gathered around, they said it was a good likeness. I later lost the drawing. Never saw it again, still wonder if anyone kept it, what stranger has it somewhere, stranger with portrait of a stranger circa 1985.

Look, the ship's sailing out of view, it's taller and thinner in the haze, in the end it looks exaggerated, more like a child's drawing than ever; even the whale's already dissolved into dirty suds, then nothing; the sea just for a moment completely empty. Teal blue – is that the colour? Teal or whatever shade of blue-green you prefer to call it, but make it deep, deep and beguiling.

And admit it – how many times have you wanted to jump right into the sea all swollen like that; no warning, no knowing when or if but to just let yourself fall from this height from these very rocks, yes, to step out over and into, to trust nothing, to tell no one, not even the person you want to take with you, only inches from your hand, only your body dropping, noticed as briefly as a glint before it disappears into that vast silence, sudden screams above you, children's, not your own, remember you'd been with strangers watching a whale disperse when you jumped, light snatched, lips, arse tight against the volume of water trying to get you to swallow, salt stinging your throat, stronger than any spill you remember over an old chip supper, hands and feet already flapping like hell, working like never before, UP, UP, no dignity or need to ponder on how you must now look changing your mind, no need to tell you that under all that water there is of course no shoal of beautiful silver fish forming patterns like arrows that lead you to a neatly made-up king-size bed, there is no bed waiting for you to fold back the satin red coverlet, *what were you thinking* as you dare to emerge so quickly air-starved, not the first or last time you cannot return an answer to the sound of your name thrown over you, a loved one screeching alongside a stranger's children ... What *shtik*; what an undignified entrance, laughter taken this way and that on the force of the next and the next wave.

Home – dry yourself off. The urge to stay put in an almost anonymous little town.

Home – the evening newspapers read: *21 people arrested on terrorist charges.*

Critical ... it repeats in the headlines ...
Be a little cautious
Things maybe imminent
Identify the main players
The highest levels of alert
Take necessary precautions
Maintain a sense of threat
Severe or red
Intent and capability
Various senses developed
Assemble
devices
strategies
These ideas have been around for a long time now
Our homes are safe, they say
Safer than they were before
Despite the fact that there are still people in our country who want to hurt us
These are desperate people, despicable times ...

Today I find The Kiss.

Count people I have never met before. Seven of us gather. A small crowd I join at the museum, pushing myself in as if I belonged to this party of strangers, in toward the body of this unexpected Kiss allowed out of its seclusion … For a temporary display, or so they tell us. Trying hard to concentrate on what's here in front of me, having to admit that after waiting so many months to see it, when it finally appears of course I am pleased, a smug greeting of sorts, an end to impatience; yet when I enter the room, eager enough with the news of its return, yes, as I take my place alongside the others it is not The Kiss that pulls my eye, instead it is a painting to its far left that dominates. A painting – more a *colour* – that I cannot stop looking at: the striking blue of Renoir's *La Parisienne,* his petite Blue Lady, recognised, remembered. Like the portrait of Picasso's *Woman in Blue, Mujer en Azul* that I saw at the Reina Sofía Museum in Madrid just weeks back, also unexpected, something that again arrested me. A painting and a dress I would like to have kept. A colour and a dress I would like to look at each day. Either painting would do, dress, colour, figure; Picasso's blue more like a woman in green; Renoir's blue that cannot be denied, a blue lady overlooking a Kiss.

And when this Kiss finally appears, do I want to take possession of it, shoo these others aside, to be alone to examine it fully, at last? I wish I could say that I did, wish I could admit to affection for these lovers, for Rodin. Wish I could admit to changing my mind, to say that any previous disregard for them was a lie. For sure it is still not easy to look upon them at all, to look this close, to stand for any length of time beside them. Yet being part of the group of seven who mill around both reassures and confirms that old adage that there is safety in numbers, in sharing a look, in the anonymity museums allow,

298

in the freedom I have to stand here quietly composing a letter to you, maybe my last letter to you, early morning, all the early mornings that have passed between us, all the words from me to you that have come and gone, been erased, mornings over the months since your letter arrived, prompting my first tentative steps; the day still to come, telling myself that having found The Kiss I will take this as the much-needed sign that gives me permission to stop. Final whelps. Your letter to En that kissed us both: X marks the spot. That makes me laugh, the realisation that *of course* most letters end this way: with love – with a X, that final reiteration, a scratch no better than you deciding not to sign your name. In this case I sign my name but have no way to reach you. Despite this I should strive to finish as expected, as is courteous, loving and polite – to end with a kiss…Maybe two XX, like the two here kissing… No need to go on with that… This is what I say, I read letters, I count kisses … didn't I tell you this already? Saying to myself, let The Kiss be the end of this X between us. The kisses of your letter that brought me back to the museum to search out the couple that won't stop kissing; the safety of the museum, each day the same routine, patterns of waking and walking, the reassurance of recognising a building I have a great fondness for, familiarity at its root – the *family*; the small journey through the park to see again; on the way, each time, the man who photographs the leaves in the sun, the leaves in the sun pure green that turn red, fall and reform. What happens when it rains? He is still there waiting. Look! The young man with his camera held to the light. The story he'll tell you, if you pause a while, of the artist who installed headsets and microphones into the hearts of trees. Said, you could hear the trees talk. Deep in their guts, in the wood, they'd groan, whisper, cry. The headphones dangled from the branches like flowers awaiting pollination, awaiting a human ear pressing itself against a tree speaking: listen … and to what? The auscultation of trees. Imagine buying a stethoscope, placing it to objects, random hearts, the home you can make in trees, parks, public benches, paths, here in this museum, warm hues, even for hours, where you begin to recognise people you never knew, people you have no need to speak to, or if you do, it binds you to nothing; fleeting contact, no contract, no categories or future wiles.

The patterns of the museum guards, their shifts, their ways of walking, pacing, a uniform comforts and breaks the morning into reassuring divvies. The different weight and sounds that steps make both relaxes and tenses these keepers who might look and acknowledge others; some who take their leisure and their jobs more literally and prefer – or feel they should – to stare at some point off the map, some imaginary unidentifiable point in time and space, preferring not to confront either the public or the artworks with the directness of an eye; some show no preference for anything here. Here there is no hierarchy, inanimate or living, neither would you know for sure what feelings others might have for The Kiss. The Kiss denied, now given, the kisses of your letter, false kisses, words we no longer read, nor would want again, the ellipsis of the kiss, the kiss of greeting and parting, who would begin to guess my reason for standing here before this Kiss, before these six others, counting me that makes seven, no doubt with seven different reasons for being here, maybe more than one reason per person, who could do the maths or write the fiction, who can assume our innocence here.

The museum guard assigned to our room is smiling at me as if he catches my thoughts. I want to say to him, I wish you wouldn't look at me looking. And what will I say if he steps forward, moves from smiling to asking, What are you looking for in The Kiss? He, who no doubt has already made assumptions about my interest in this bronze embrace, easy romantic notions, like the slight blush I felt rising when I first came to ask in which place I might find these two lovers. Hesitation; concern that others would too quickly fill in a narrative I cannot defend, too quickly ask, *what lost love or heartbreak pulls you here?* One of the seven tells us that schoolchildren wrote letters to the museum – not to this one but to London's Tate, where another Kiss awaits. Their Kiss made from Pentelican marble, she says, cooler to the eye, one of the three versions Rodin made in his lifetime; young women, barely eighteen, and even younger schoolchildren confessing in their letters how seeing The Kiss had helped them find a language for sex... Imagine!

How many more have stood before these two with a tear, longing, daydreams, first loves, the disdain I've always had for this Kiss never far from return. What does the man who guards them dream of when they are alone, the three of them, with only the nakedness of the room and the whir of the humidifier, the dark seal of the solid brass doors gleaming, before the public arrive. The hush of feathers, the daily tickle on a Kiss made clean for another day, from a cleaner who ensures these two are dust-free, a woman who has gone unnoticed. The three of them left alone now, the guard and the two who won't ever look his way, despite the quiet and whatever permission he now allows himself to stare hard and long; free for a while at least of censorship, of witness, they will not uncurl nor include him while they kiss on, not caring a damn for whatever awkward confessions he has on his lips.

For sure the man who guards The Kiss is unable to guess my reason for being here, and how to begin to explain... To explain how your words drew me here so far back, or so it now seems; and what would be the point of beginning this story again, to go back to those first pages, the letter, the bed, the phone ringing in my ear, En's voice. How could the guard know that it was less an interest in these two that had me rushing

301

around this building to seek them out, but more an impulse, like kissing the Blarney Stone, some kind of charm I was after or seeking – is that it? When I hadn't previously noticed any charm in The Kiss – yes, maybe now a charm of the lucky kind, the kind you might have rattling on a bracelet, The Kiss made into a tiny silver charm, next to an old boot, or horseshoe, no better end than to have these two jingling on the end of a key ring, the fortune to have got this far, with them, with you, safe and sound; the certainty that these two kiss regardless of the time we did or did not have with each other, kiss on regardless of whatever drama might ensue around them, petty squabble, tart words, whatever genial words we might attempt to put back in place, whatever rumpus and flub, whatever hope of appeasement. These two who will no doubt outlive us all, kiss on after our death, after our children's passing, on and on they kiss: *bedlam, becalm*. Unless someone were to force them apart, shatter them to tiny pieces, but not be surprised if, however much you try and part these two, by whatever means, they would always be found stuck together, a hand forever wedded to a thigh. Unless we were, God forbid, to smelt them to a liquid separation. These two, all over the world replicated ad infinitum, they Kiss here in spotlights, kissing in the dark, after hours, even in exile, with their mix of different materials and shades and colours, not unlike the assorted colours of eyes upon them, eyes both closed and open, fleeting shifts, even the blind visit, touch in ways we have not yet dared to try, kiss on regardless of how long it takes me to put all these words to you together – and still no destination, no known address – as if it matters any more. These two hold each other's breath while so much is remembered and forgotten, remember to forget, forget to remember you.

I want to say again, it's not easy to look, *especially* at a kiss, and it's not easy to feign such concentration, such attention to detail, such commitment and patience. Do you misread me sir, I want to ask the man guarding them, but more than that I want instead to lower my eyes, to move on. Try not to read anything else into his silent insistence. We circle again, for something to do, the sound of steps on the perfect block floor like an agreement, an undertaking to move, to witness; shuffle as close as possible to The Kiss, still here, us, them, the loyal.

Just look at us!

Imagine us flying, circling the top of The Kiss like blue birds the colour of the painted lady's dress. We do not cover them in waste as common pigeons might. We twitter, sing, hover over The Kiss. It's easier now to follow a man shifting his weight onto his other leg; he's drifted off to follow his wife. Let's say they have momentarily reduced the seven of us to five. It is easier to follow them around the room; yes, it would be easier to follow them away from this circle of eager eyes, away from this endless song and snog – snog – what a word, take a moment to look it up: *How to kiss a girl*, it says, *learn how to kiss. Cuddle, fondle, smooch, necking*, it is easier to return to the *Blue Lady*, to the darkness of Whistler's paintings, the skirts of *The Faggot Pickers* gathering sticks, the women's skirts filled with orange light, The Kiss again.

The darkness of tarnished bronze gives The Kiss a rather cumbersome quality, as if it was carved from coal. The lump of black shiny coal mother would take me to see as a child, coal hidden away in the park where beside it others took their practice at first kisses, next to Monkey Puzzle, the vicious swans and the broken swings. The lump of coal unformed into any shape, just an enormous block displayed under a small red corrugated roof, a little open-sided shelter where inside coal was slowly displaced, shrunk, eaten away over the years by rain, fingers, picnic spoons, boy's penknives, birds and squirrels. Imagine, again, burning The Kiss. What flames, what smoke for days and miles, to cremate it on a bed of papers, balls of idle news, lay it on sticks, sugar to make it flare, to ask, what colours a kiss? What colours is a kiss capable of?

One of the seven – currently five – still faithful to her vigil, leans closer, confides that she was on an aeroplane once … Listen to this! The atmosphere was jovial. It was an airline that went to a lot of trouble to keep the passengers entertained. To pass the time the cabin crew decided they'd get the passengers involved in a little game. Passing around lipsticks and tissues. Asking everyone in turn if they would apply the lipstick and then blot the tissue. Something we have all watched our mothers do, applying the lipstick confidently, top lip, right side, left side, the bottom lip one continuous sweep of red, blot decisively. The tissues were collected, she said. The captain, taking a needed rest between take off and lunch, decided on and held up the best kiss. People clapped. We all have our stories …

The man and his wife rejoin us, but two into seven never goes. I assume that much of them, that they are married. Unlike these two who kiss, the two who wandered away have an air of thirty years about them, hard labour, weekend passes, have begun to resemble each other. They re-form us back to my lucky number as the wife, pronouncing French with ease, explains that The Kiss was originally commissioned for *The Gates of Hell*, for the entrance to the *Musée des Arts Décoratifs*. A door commissioned for a building that never existed, that would never exist, doors that went nowhere. The couple based on Dante's *Paolo and Francesca*. Rodin's cousin, one of the first people to see the gates Rodin had locked himself away to work on, asked, – And this immense wooden cabinet that rises to the ceiling taking up so much space, what is that? Rodin answered quietly, – It's my door. The sound of these words can break your heart, the woman says.

The couple discussing The Kiss don't kiss – well, not in our

304

company, even though I feel they should – maybe we all should, what better place, but no need to go back to that. They seem in no rush to leave; come to that, none of us seem to have any concern to leave each other's sides, the seven of us who form and reform ourselves into the chance circle we have become, bringing to mind an image of a fairy ring of wild mushrooms sprouting around a standing stone. One of the seven remarks that even though some suggest it's a kiss on the verge of kissing, an interrupted kiss, if you walk around the back of the sculpture there's a spot at which you can see the actual point of contact, the kiss of The Kiss. When The Kiss was first displayed, separated from its door, their figures were made bigger than ever imagined, people were shocked at the nakedness, various versions of The Kiss hidden behind a curtain, covered in tarpaulin, hidden in the ignominy of a stable block. In how many museum basements have these two been bound and held in the dark. So many versions on, their various destinations mirror Dante's lovers stabbed by Francesca's jealous husband, entombed together, and another infinite embrace doubles under our feet.

Each of us now takes an unequal turn to move closer: we squat, stretch, peep, point, discuss the muscles of Paolo's back. The variations. Begin to notice patches of orange, polished bronze, deep green turning black; Rodin's elaborate signature, the swirl of Rodin's R etched into metallic rock, a rock the couple rests eternally upon. The male figure's foot dissolves beneath the foot of the woman he kisses. The hands and thighs of the male look exaggerated and out of proportion. Someone says, and we all agree, that his torso is too stiff, his hand discarding or clinging on to the book that was said to have enflamed the couple's passion, the story of *Lancelot and Guinevere* held behind Francesca's back. Some take turns to trace Rodin's name with their fingertips. Paolo's fingertips pressed tentatively on to Francesca's thigh. We take turns to gaze again between the crack in the embrace where the kiss of The Kiss is visible. Witness again the kiss that won't stop kissing. The suggestion of her hair pinned into a bun. From this angle her small breasts are not visible. Someone says it looks from here as if it were two men kissing. That changes everything about the cliché it's become.

It is then that the guard who walks the room speaks, his voice expectant, known, as if sensing that I am waiting to be singled out, to be asked the question I so fear: What brought you here today, what causes someone to hog a Kiss this way? What a word, to hog the snog, to smile as if guilty of something unavoidable. Agree to say *nothing*. Feel seven bodies, all caught out, become one muscle as taut as Paolo's thigh tightening to the touch of Francesca's raised leg. The sound of the guard clearing his throat, an expected probe, a gruffness, finally a surprisingly fleeting gentle reprimand that only instructs – We are not allowed to touch! That we must – Please step away! And with that, of course, we pull back, obedient, arms to our sides, folded, eyes down, no lucky numbers to call back a lost smile or two, hands thrust deep into pockets, and the pocket-less lock hands behind their backs the way royalty might. We stay put, caught out on his *please*, on the shame of reserve, the shame of taking from these two what was never ours to assume.

Not that this lasts long. Not that he repeats.

It is no longer a question of saying yes or no to him, only that our eyes moving to and from The Kiss are complicit, a silent agreement that the tracks of light that lay bare both bodies too clearly evidence all the stray hands that have defied the museum's law: *Thou shalt not touch*. Impossible rules, we say with our eyes again widening – no need to speak. Not now. Just an affirmation of all those that have pulled themselves back, only to reach out again as swiftly as a kiss, as compelled as a guard who must remain in motion, a museum law that a guard must turn and turn again, survey other corners, police other hands, turn his back while we quickly edge forward. Both hindered and reassured by the side we happen to find ourselves upon, by the seconds we have, we do not begin anew, but seven of us reach for well-worn paths: the nearest thigh, the ends of toes, the lower back, the book Paolo holds, Francesca's hair. I should say that there are places no one ventures to touch on these bodies, dark nooks that only small children have the indifference to stray into, the courage to map, sticky prints too incoherent to fake. With one eye on the guard, we rush, *hush*, follow one another, soothe what an eye cannot sustain, touch and touch again The Kiss as if for luck.

X

ALSO BY ANGELA MORGAN CUTLER

AUSCHWITZ

Auschwitz: a place where millions were killed and which thousands now visit each year. A mass grave – and a tourist destination. The focus of this work of autobiographical fiction is on the sightseers – the curious that are drawn to visit. It is a book that questions our need to look: what is there to uncover, other than the difficulty of peering into such a place and into a subject that has been obsessively documented, yet can never really be understood? How to write about Auschwitz in the twenty-first century, in a time when the last generation of survivors is soon to be lost?

This is also a book that searches for a personal story. It opens on a local bus that takes Angela, her husband En (whose mother survived the holocaust where most of her family did not) and their two sons to Auschwitz sixty years after the holocaust, and ends in a pine forest outside Minsk where En's grandparents were shot in May 1942.

The backbone of Auschwitz is a series of e-mails between the author and acclaimed American writer Raymond Federman. At the age of 14, Federman (who died at the age of 81, in 2009) was hastily thrust into the small upstairs closet of their Paris apartment by his mother just before she, his father and two sisters were taken to Auschwitz, where they were killed. Federman also has spent a lifetime trying to find a language appropriate for the enormity of the holocaust and his part in its legacy, ultimately espousing laughterature – laughter as a means of survival.

This beautiful, powerful and innovative work experiments with new forms – correspondence, reflections, dreams, a travelogue – that mirror the fragmentary legacy of the holocaust itself and that, at the same time, capture its contradictions – and sometimes its absurdity.

Praise for Auschwitz:

'Cutler's *Auschwitz* creates a category of its own … Cutler's voice is undoubtedly a new voice of the post-Holocaust generations … Her sophisticated and highly individual poetic style "shows the tracks of her labour" … in an imaginative way and by doing so turns Cutler's debut into a superb novel on writing.'
Scottish Review of Books

'Cutler does not preach or patronise, and her ability to deliver impressively poetic prose means that she never compromises the subject-matter. Her voice is refreshing, shocking and commanding, and represents an exciting departure for contemporary fiction.'
New Welsh Review

'Auschwitz stands like a tombstone for our civilisation. Angela Morgan Cutler has brilliantly infiltrated the borders of this landscape of desolation. Somehow she has found a voice that reflects the enormity of the horrors perpetuated there without being stifled by them. Unsentimental and richly worked … the words are more than mere messengers of thoughts and feelings – they glow with a life of their own … the whole package quite inimitable: the rarest quality in literature.' *Henry Woolf*

'Cutler writes like a British Hélène Cixous. Her invitation to visit with her the tourist attraction that modern-day Auschwitz has become is daring, shocking, profoundly moving – even, on occasion, funny. I loved its stylistic hybridity.' *Susan Sellers*

'When the story of the unspeakable has been told a thousand times, when the images of the unimaginable have been shown a thousand times, when the mind is numb - where do you go from there? You have to start anew. That is what Angela Morgan Cutler has done.'
Rex Bloomstein

ISBN 978-1-906120; RRP £9.99.
Available online at www.tworavenspress.com, priced at £7.99 inc P&P in the UK, £9.99 inc P&P overseas.

Two Ravens Press is the most remote literary publisher in the UK, operating from a working croft by the sea, right at the end of the most westerly road on the Isle of Lewis in the Outer Hebrides. Our approach to publishing is as radical as our location: Two Ravens Press is run by two writers with a passion for language and for books that are non-formulaic and that take risks. We publish cutting-edge and innovative contemporary fiction, nonfiction and poetry.

Visit our website for comprehensive information on all of our books and authors – and for much more:

- browse all Two Ravens Press books (print books and e-books too) by category or by author, and purchase them online at an average 20% discount on retail price, post & packing-free (in the UK, and for a small fee overseas)

- there is a separate page for each book, including summaries, extracts and reviews, and one for each of our authors, including interviews, biographies and photographs

- you can also find us on Facebook: become a fan of the Two Ravens Press page, and automatically receive all our news and updates about new books.

www.tworavenspress.com